CW00551145

A007840179

WITHDRA
FOR
SALE

)8

CHESHIRE

LIBRARIES

20 MAR 1996

| BKD | 2382 |

9

PROVINCIAL PLEASURES

20 MAR 1958

PROVINCIAL PLEASURES

Norman Nicholson

ILLUSTRATED BY B. BIRO

BOOKCASE
17 Castle Street, Carlisle

© IRVINE HUNT 1959

First published in Great Britain 1959
Reprinted 1993

Published by Bookcase, 17 Castle Street, Carlisle
Printed by The Amadeus Press, Huddersfield, West Yorkshire
ISBN 0 9519920 4 X

To
MY WIFE

NOTE

The town of Odborough is by no means imaginary, though some of it no longer appears quite as it is described in this book. The characters, however, are all my own invention, except for that of my father, whom I could not have invented since he invented me.

N. N.

Contents

January

THE BEST way to see the New Year in is to be fast asleep. I do not enjoy a First of January which starts with a headache.   So New Year's Eve is a night for early to bed and never care whether next year comes or not.

There is still plenty of time, however, to take a last look at last year's world before the first-footing processions begin.

I walk to the dormer window of my attic bedroom from which, like a cave-dweller, half-way up a cliff, I can watch the tidal movements of the street below.   It is a warm, moist, muzzy night.   A wave of Atlantic air, sweating with fogs, washes round the base of Black Fell as it rears itself, unseen in the darkness, like a harbour mole above the town.

The fine rain seems not so much to be falling as to be floating, drifting, even steaming, upwards.   Hold out your hand and you can feel not a drop, yet the sleeve of your coat is found to be damp.   The street-lamps are no longer points or splinters of light. They are absorbed entirely into the blur of mist, so that the black

cliffs of the street are lit as with a phosphorescence, a faint underwater light in which shapes undulate and bulge and only shadows
have any solidity.

St Kentigern's Terrace is, at a first glance, empty.   Beyond the
gently-shelving slope of the street, the mist swirls and brightens,
to reveal, bold as breakwaters, the three Banks of the Market
Square.   Above them, like a lighthouse, shines the Market Clock,
seeming to have lifted itself clear of the spray and smudge of the
rain.   I cannot see it from here, but I do see the light from it lying
flat and steady on the roofs of the house opposite, grey-washing
the squares of slates, lining the edges of skylight and dormer.
So that here, among the roofs, lifted high above the swish of the
street, here is a solid world.   The roof-line is the level of the land.
Below, submarine, the streets are carved in channels up which the
town's tide flows.   I can hear the first murmur of it already as the
ebb begins to turn at the dip of the year.   The tide flows through
the streets as through a delta, through gulley and creek and back-
water, along the main canals of Waterloo Street and Trafalgar
Road and Furnace Road, full into the harbour of the Market
Square.

It is not an impersonal tide as in the cities, where each person is
caught up in one huge flood, cast on the shingle of one wave and
sucked back by the next.   It is, instead, a gently healing flow,
bringing life daily as the sea brings life to mussel and barnacle.
It misses no one. It flows up the narrow streets, drenching the
dreams of children, packed two and three in a bed in back-room
and attic; it seeps up the stairs where an old woman lies in a
widowhood of candlelight; it washes through shops and pubs and
chapels and schools.   There is nothing anonymous about it.   It
hisses as it flows in a fume of names, whispering in porch and
doorway, in alley and arch and entry, through back-yard and
back-garden and allotment and vicarage lawn and along the new-
laid grass of Festival Avenue.   Everywhere the foam shapes itself
into faces, evanescent as bubbles, yet instantly known.   There is
a spume of faces, scudding down the street or bubbling high as the
chimney-pots and bursting on the bedroom windows.

' Ah, would you?' shouts Mrs Makeweight, the butcher's wife, as she catches sight of Councillor Quorum watching her in her nightie. And she skelly-eyes the mirror and knows that he wouldn't.

There is no cold-shouldering of those faces, no turning a deaf ear to those names. The three Miss Snoots of Mount Pleasant, who, for thirty years, have refused to nod or speak to at least seven thousand nine hundred and fifty of the town's eight thousand inhabitants, now see the tide rise in wave after impertinent wave up the steep hill of Old Odborough until it spits against the very drawing-room casement. The faces billow against the glass insisting on being noticed, anxious to be recognised. They surge in a hundred sea-calls of reminder:

' I sat next to you in Standard One.'

' I stuck a pen-nib in your arm.'

' I postman's-knocked you in the Bible Christian Sunday School.'

For this is the tide of the past as well as of the present. The voices of those who are dead in the high-and-dry of the church-yard call once again in the roar of the tide. Half-forgotten names and half-forgotten events are flushed through the brains of the town. And more which are quite forgotten, which lie beyond the grave of even the oldest memory, even those are not unvisited by this tide. Those who notched their acts on the walls of the town —who planted trees and dug ditches; who sowed the comfrey that still grows in the back of the vicarage garden; who smashed the lamp-post that is still unmended, in the broken-down street beside the slag-bank; who set up the flag-pole in the Jubilee Field and hung the bells in St Kentigern's Church and fixed the buzzer at the Ironworks and scratched ' RUM ' on the freestone sill of the Temperance Hall—none of them is forgotten by this. Tide and time wait for every man.

.   .   .

My eyes are tingling as from salt spray. The glowing circles of the street-lamps swirl in whirlpools of watery milk. I return to my bed and lie down, and let the sound of the New Year tide rumour and grumble in the street below me.

The Market Clock strikes half-past eleven.

They are gathering now in the Square. Only a few people at first, clustered in the shadows of the doorways. The centre of the Square, under the spray of the lights that have replaced the Jubilee Drinking Fountain, is still empty. The upstairs windows of the houses behind the shops are lit, their curtains drawn. From the Victoria Hall comes a gust of trumpets, a kick and clatter as if all the old buckets and biscuit tins of the town were being rolled across a bouldery shore. The door of *The Prince of Wales* gapes open and out blows a breath of beer and extended licence. The gloss of the vestibule glows a clean, pale, aspidistra-green, as if electricity had never been invented and every bracket was still alight in a pride of gas-mantles.

Violet Moss stands at the Jubilee Road corner of the Square, in the shadow of the Liverpool Bank. She is with her father and mother and her sister, yet she is quite alone. She is afraid, at the moment, that she will always be alone. Yet the thought that perhaps she may not be alone perturbs her still more. She watches the crowds spilling into the Square—jostling and inter-cepting, grouping and splitting up, butting in and cutting out like molecules in a chemical formula. Without quite seeing, without having ever quite seen, she is somehow aware of the nearnesses within the swirl of mist and mackintoshes—the slap and tickle, the pinch and predacities. She moves a little way apart from the others, closer to the Bank railings, wrapping its shadow round her like a cloak. She puts her hands against her cheeks holding them almost as if she had toothache. The greenish, slanting light draws lines down her face, as in the stage make-up for an old woman. Almost as if she herself could see this, she begins to play the part. The rivulets of pleasure dry up within her blood. She is no longer sixteen. She is a spinster of fifty, her face stiff with fascinated repulsion at all she sees and does not see in the Square. If midnight does not strike, if the bird does not whistle from the dark chimney-pots, if the angel does not hail her, then that is how she will look for ever.

Her sister creeps up and tickles her under the arms.

It is a quarter to twelve now. The green four-face of the clock, like a huge illuminated flower-head of the wild moschatel, blooms into the rain. The Odborough Royal Temperance Band is assembling outside *The Prince of Wales*. Each bandsman props his music into the little stand that juts out close to the mouthpiece. An effort of cheering is heard, purposeless and forced. A late bus edges slowly into the Square, pushing its way through the crowd. A night-flying sea-bird pipes above the roof-tops.

The Rev. Canon Olds looks out of the parlour window of St Kentigern's Vicarage down the church drive towards the Square. Trees fork and double against the street-lights, and branches seem to run like cracks across the face of the Market Clock. The light from the parlour window falls on the heavy unmown dead grass that borders the drive where laurels and hollies push forward their cowled heads like eavesdroppers.

Dr Olds is preoccupied. He notices neither the lights from the Square nor the overshadowing cliff-side of the church. There is a choice to be made, as there always is every New Year's Eve—a choice which will colour his mind for many months. If he could choose next year's weather the choice would not be more important. He lays the three books side by side on the top of the bookshelf : Dante, Ariosto, Tasso. This year it shall be Italian. Every morning, except Sundays, Lent, and days when there is an early celebration—every morning, after his prayers and the Bible, there is to be half an hour of Dante or Ariosto or Tasso. It will be read slowly, a page or two a day, with a dictionary on the pillow beside him and a translation to refer to if necessary. Dante or Ariosto or Tasso? Shall he move through the dark of February, descending deeper and deeper into hell down the terrace of the slag-bank, to see Paolo and Francesca blown about in the smoke from the furnace or Satan frozen in the sump behind the gas-works; or, as he emerges from under the railway into the marsh at the foot of Purgatory, to pluck the ' giunchi sopra il molle limo ', sea-plantain or scurvy grass or maybe Dutch rush, washed by the seepage of the tide ? Or shall he go forward into the spring with Ariosto, watching Olympia stranded naked on the rocks of Odborough Point, with the ore-red sea staining her limbs as with blood ? Or again, in summer, with Fairfax as a crib, shall he behold deserts about him and enchanted shrubberies and a sky scoured by blown sand, and Jerusalem, still undelivered, shining in a glory of chimney-pots and chapel ventilators?

Ten to twelve. The bell-ringers are walking up the drive. The Square is rapidly filling with people. In Rotting Road, in a bed-room that looks across the allotments to the Jubilee Pleasure Gardens, John Dodder lives, trying to persuade himself that his brain is as sleepy as his legs, which have not been awake for fifteen years. The window is shut tight and blankets are scarfed around his head, half smothering him. Desperately he determines not to notice the footsteps or the voices, or the cheering when it starts, or the church bells. He will ignore it all : he will sleep first.

' It is not the New Year till I wake up,' he says. ' It is not the New Year till I wake up.'

Five to twelve. A dozen people are gathering for Watch-Night service in the Bible Christian Chapel in Trafalgar Road. The minister is bringing his short address to a close. Soon he will begin the prayer which is to lead into the New Year. Contralto Ethel sits alone in the choir, her old face wrapped like the withered outer leaves of a cabbage round a centre that is still green as a salad. The almost empty chapel is before her—Jacobean-stained pews, umbrella stands, the red hymn-books in the back seat, the great brown honeycombs of the gallery.

The ten or twelve in the congregation, scattered so widely about the church that they are scarcely within shouting distance of one another, are growing restless. Wrists twitch watches into view. Without bothering to look behind at the hymn-board Ethel opens her book at the next hymn. There is no one in the congregation whom she did not know as a child, yet there is not one under fifty. The New Year is the time when you feel old. The New Year is a time for remembering.

.   .   .

The Market Clock strikes. Violet Moss's sister kisses her father. A cheer begins, raucous, ironical, from those on the edge of the crowd. The Ironworks buzzer to-wit-to-whoos as the first minute emerges like a mouse from its hole. In the middle of the Square there is a dim, indiscriminate scrimmage of Happy-New-Yearing.

' Want a mouth-wash after that lot,' says Chunker Wilson.

The tenor bell syncopates into tune all by itself, greeting the year as if it were a fire.

Dr Olds stretches out his hand without more hesitation and picks up the book.

> 'Canto l'arme pietose e'l Capitano
> Che'l gran sepolcro liberò di Cristo———'

he reads. Then he writes inside the cover : ' The Rev. Canon Olds, Circumcision, 19——— Address for the next 12 months—

> ' St Kent's Vicarage
> Jerusalem.'

The crowd, arm-linked and knotted together in a bootlace tangle, tries to form a circle. *Auld Lang Syne* is heaved into the air as if the tune were being tossed in a blanket. Daphne Huggins is swung by the arm-pits clean off her feet. Screams and high-heel shoes skitter across the pavement.

The six bells dive off together, belly-flapping and splashing all at once into the middle of the peal. Sudden as an explosion, the band drums up and blazes away down the Terrace into Rotting Road.

' Not till I wake up,' says John Dodder. ' Not till I've slept. It's still December. It's still last year. Not till I wake up.'

They are singing, now, in the Chapel:

> 'Come let us anew
> Our journey pursue,
> Roll round with the year,
> And never stand still till the Master appear.'

The crowd in the Square begins to whirl round and round like water in a pot-hole, continually throwing off little splashes and dribbles which trickle away down St Kentigern's Terrace or along Jubilee Road or over the Railway Bridge to Old Odborough. But the centre of the whirl, as if held by some half-drunken centrifugal force, remains together in a pool of shadows and voices.

B

Now it begins to wash down and up the Square.   It forms itself
into a wave, and crests and breaks and goes flowing down the
Terrace back along the channels of the town.   The year's first
tide is on the ebb.

> 'Our life is a dream;
> Our time, as a stream,
> Glides swiftly away;
> And the fugitive moment refuses to stay.'

Charles Wesley's anapaests dip and flutter over the empty
pews.

Contralto Ethel sits alone in the stalls that were once packed
tight with cheerful songsters.   Fifty years ago there was not a
baritone in the circuit she hadn't kissed, not a tenor she hadn't
turned down.   Many a Pleasant Sunday Afternoon had been
made pleasanter by Ethel, and at Faith Suppers she saw faith
rewarded.   In those days, plump and sweet as one of her own
middle notes, she had seen the chapel full of Cornishmen—
miners from the tin-mines who had come to Odborough to prize
the iron-ore out of the rocks like a mussel out of its shell.   Quickly
they had taken charge, as wood-bosses, enginemen, and underground captains.   They brought their ministers with them and
built their own chapels—Wesleyan, Primitive, Bible Christian.
They became local preachers, circuit stewards, Sunday-school
teachers.   A boy, leaving school, would let himself be seen at
chapel for one or two weeks before applying for a job at the mines.
Cornish voices defied the Cumberland accent for year after year.
Cornish pasties and Devonshire cream replaced the Cumberland
Squares and the Easterman Giant herb pudding.   And like the
Welsh, who had their own tin chapel in Furnace Road, the
Cornishmen sang.

As Ethel's eyes hazed over, the electric bulbs mellowed to gas-
lamps and the chapel was full again, packed floor to gallery, the
air hot with breath.   The moisture ran down the painted walls;
texts and hymn numbers and fleur-de-lys steamed like a greenhouse.   Old Pa Penaluna, who wore a boy's cap in chapel to
keep the draught off his bald head, sweated till his beard was wet
as a sponge.   The congregation roared the Watch-Night tunes

and the boys in the blower's loft nearly ruptured themselves with pumping as the music whistled out of the bellows.

> 'The arrow is flown;
> The moment is gone;
> The millenial year
> Rushes on to our view, and eternity's here.'

The organist pulls out new stops, and, as in a change of manual, Ethel feels her thoughts falter and alter. Her seventy-year-old voice returns to the task of leading the little crocodile of voices along the winding path of the tune. The empty pews hurt her like an amputation. The New Year, she thinks to herself, has more of the look of an end than of a beginning.

.   .   .

But, while this first tide of the year ebbs along the channels of the streets, what can the town itself remember? Here, in my attic bed, high above the backwash of the streets, I feel a deeper tide flow over me—a five-hundred-million-year tide, at the bottom of which the town and its people lie like grains of sand, like dregs in a teapot. Here, among chimney-pots and aerials, I feel the weight of the tides of the Ordovician Age—slow estuarine tides in which the mud sank and settled to form the rock which is now heaped in a hill above the town. In the night ebb Black Fell becomes once again a dark underwater rock scoured by the tides.

Then in a jiffy of millennia the sea begins to simmer. Volcanoes break out like carbuncles. A red-hot pus of lava bursts through the under-skin of the ocean, and the vapour stinks and fumes, boiling in tidal waves against the coasts. Under-sea deluges of ash stain the water black as a sewer where the cooled lava creates a new, slag-like landscape. Slowly under the scrubbing and bludgeoning of the tide, lava and ash, in their turn, consolidate to rock, and in the fishless seas there begins to take shape what one day will be known as Scafell or Langdale Pikes.

Once more the seas decline to sluggish shallows and the mud dreams itself into hills as gentle as the swash of its own tides. For 300 million years ago almost all that goes to make the outer

landscape of Odborough was already formed if not yet shaped—
Black Fell, the volcanic mountains of the Lakes, and the low
Silurian hills across the Dunner Estuary.   Even the town itself
was beginning to form, like bones within an embryo.

In the rocks which would make up the hill of Old Odborough
waited the stones which would make up the houses and inns and
chapels of new Odborough.   And in the hills of Furness, across the
estuary, the strata were still uncleaved which one day, as I lie in
bed, will slate the roof above my head.

Yet this is not all that remains in the memory of the town's
bones.   Down beneath the sea it all went once again, and the
tide flowed over it, warm and white as milk.   Coral bloomed on
the sea-floor in rhododendrons of stone, and a slow snow-storm of
calcium descended through the water.   The limestone which
emerged when the seas had ebbed and steamed away is scarcely
visible around the town—only a few clawings of rock at Odborough Point, where the River Dunner meets the sea.   Yet it
was in this stone that the town quickened into life.   For
the iron-ore in the veins of the rock infused blood into the bones
so that here, out of the belly of the mines, the town was brought
forth.   Every Odborough child is joined by an umbilical cord,
stretching back through the ooze to the shelled, creeping creatures
of the warm lagoons.

.   .   .

Christopher Crackenthwaite walks out of the Watch-Night
service.   He had once been Choir Master and had conducted
Messiah, *Crucifixion*, and innumerable Harvest Festival anthems
till, as he himself said, his butterfly-wing collar knew as well as he
did when to twitch the tenors in.   As a young man he had been
excited by the chapel.   He had found an odd satisfaction in its
athletic puritanism; had enjoyed with sincerity his half-ironic
hypocrisies.   But with middle age the old tunes rang flat in his
ears, the old hypocrisies became merely a habit.   The choir had
dwindled to two basses, Ethel, and a pewful of kids to sing soprano.
He resigned and spent his Sunday evenings in the Working Men's
—'Feasting I watch' and a pint of mild.   But with that devil of

perversity which to him is still the moving spirit of religion, he persists in attending the most uncomfortable service of the year— liking it best, perhaps, when the night is cold, wet, and bleak.

The wave of singing is now beginning to pour down Trafalgar Road, as Christopher Crackenthwaite rolls slowly to a standstill, and remains, undisturbed as a huge sea-rubbed boulder, while the wave breaks and bisects on either side of him. A young man, adhering like a strand of wet sea-weed to a buttress of young girls, greets him with drunken impertinence:

'Happy New Year, Chris. A Happy bloody New Year to you.'

'A Happy New Year to you,' says Christopher. 'And since this is a time of peace and goodwill, may I inform you that if you care to repeat your good wishes I'll throw you through Tommy Dale's shop window.'

.   .   .

Thomas Sutcliffe Dale, late Cheap and Best, stands in his darkened shop looking out across the Crown Green. Tommy Dale is not an Odborough man. On the contrary, as he himself likes to tell, he is an off-come, having lived in the town for scarcely seventy years. His father, manager of Cheap and Best, brought him to Odborough from Yorkshire, when he was only seven, but he has remained ever since stubbornly and unmistakably a Yorkshireman. It is one of the great blessings of this life, therefore, to have been christened after his mother's family, so that he can sign his cheques with the name of the greatest batsmen of our age. There were times, of course, during the career of Bradman, and even—though less resented—during that of Hutton, when his confidence was shaken. But Bradman, as he is now convinced, was a fluke, and Hutton, a pupil—Sutcliffe alone remains the indisputable master.

Tommy Dale's Yorkshire birth, together with his length of residence in the town, gives him certain privileges. Since scarcely anyone can remember an Odborough without him, it is impossible to call him an import. At the same time, as one who was born beyond the Pennines, as one who had lived above grocery shops in four different counties before he was eight years old—as such he is able, as he himself claims, to take a detached view.

'You people,' he says, striding about his shop, by the light of the lamps on the Green, the scents of ham and bacon and cheese and onions guiding him safely among the barrels and shadows:

'You people, you have been cooped all your little lives in the streets of this town. You never see beyond the lengths of your noses.'

He stops with the intuition of a blind man, within half an inch of a tower of Shredded Wheat and Lux and fire-lighters.

'I have seen Odborough grow,' he says to the midnight. 'I have seen streets blossom here and merl away there. I have seen the shoppers fill this Green like a crowd at a cricket match, and I have watched them go away again, leaving the Green as empty'—he looks across rough sodden grass under the blur of the lamps, with the half broken-down houses lounging round about—'leaving the Green as empty as a cricket field on a wet Sunday night when you've just lost the last match of the season.'

It is true that the life of a small town seems to wash up and down, to sway backward and forward from generation to generation. The great industrial cities, though they may have grown up in the nineteenth and twentieth centuries, had the basic plan of their development laid down in the Middle Ages. The church, the High Street, the ford, the bridge—these drew the first lines which centuries have not been able to rub out. But the small town, with no known history behind it, is less predictable in its way of growth. From the time of the Norman Conquest until the eighteenth century, Odborough was no more than a castle, a church, and a few poor farms or cottages. Even that castle lay a mile away from what is now the town. The site of the town was then merely 'The Mains', the Outer Demesne, marshland and rough heath or dune, not worth the labour of digging. It stretched in a parallelogram of waste, half-overlapping the Dunner Estuary. Here and there were a few dollops or drumlins of clay, left by the retreating glaciers at the end of the Ice Age, which gave round hills of fifty to seventy feet high. But for the most part, the land remained at marsh level, except at the spot where the parallelogram was hinged on to the main curve of the land. Here the rock on which the whole of the marshland lay, suddenly revealed itself, a hundred feet high, scraped to the bare bone by the ice.

It was here, with unpredictable perversity, that the first village took root. Ever since the times when the Romans withdrew from the North, this part of the coast had remained strangely isolated from the rest of England. South was the Dunner Estuary and Morecambe Bay; north, the barren coast as far as the Solway; and inland were the fells. But, in the eighteenth century, with the development of the coal trade at Whitehaven and Workington, a certain amount of traffic began to trickle along the coast through Odborough : pedlars, tramps, carters with grain or coal, drovers leading Scotch or Irish cattle down to the Lancashire markets. They came to Odborough, crossed the estuary at low tide, then by Furness and Cartmel and the sands of Morecambe Bay. So an inn or two was built to accommodate them. Not, as one might have expected, on the inland sheltered side of the hill but right along the top—the road hoisting itself a hundred feet on one side and slithering down again on the other, though with a deviation of less than a furlong it could have kept to level ground. *The Ship* was there in 1745 and claims to have accommodated John Wesley. *The Pilot* employed a man to act as guide to travellers across the shifting sands of the Dunner.

So Old Odborough established itself—a knotty, stretched, tailend of a street, trailing over the hump of the hill. Below it, still, was nothing but marsh, sandy pasture, and the sod-and-cobble hovels of the forty-acre farmers.

It was in the middle of the nineteenth century that the new town began—when iron-ore was discovered at Odborough Point. At first, development was cautious—the prospectors had no idea of the enormous deposits of ore which lay beneath the line of the high tide. The first miners lodged in Old Odborough. The first new houses were built there, along the old road over the hill. It was no hardship to the men in those days to have to walk two miles either way to work, and they wanted the company of the older houses and inns—they did not fancy living in lonely huts or terraces out on the windy Mains, among the new sores of the

mines.   The railway came and set its station at the bottom of the
hill, and indeed, named it Odborough Hill, after the hill rather
than the town, for Odborough still remained primarily the name
of the Castle.   The old road from *The Ship* and *The Pilot* now
became the Main Street.   Other inns were built and a bank and
new houses—all of them more like farm-buildings jutting out from
the hillside than the beginnings of a town.   There were no terraces, no villas, no gardens.   Every building was improvised;
walls, gables, roof-end, porches, conglomerated side by side, haphazard as a rockery.   Then the first shops appeared.   Cheap and
Best, anxious to stake their share in the new enterprise, opened
their stores at the foot of Old Odborough, opposite *The Railway
Hotel*.

Here the main road from Lancashire entered the town, forking
left from Odborough Hill, and right, over the level-crossing
towards the offices and the mines.   As the manager of the stores
watched the farmers driving in to market and the bosses driving in
to work, he felt certain that he was right in the heart of this newly
come-of-age town, with his hand on the wallet above that heart.

But the town was only at the beginning of its growth.   In the
1860s new deposits of ore were discovered, and new shafts sunk.
Blast furnaces were opened at the other corner of the parallelogram, looking up the estuary.   Miners and labourers came in by
the hundred—from the dales round about, from Cornwall and
Wales and Ireland.   The little houses and inns of Old Odborough
were packed to bursting, and a dozen sects and dialects slashed
and convulsed together.   Builders came.   A quarry was opened.
New houses sprang up out of the stone of Old Odborough on the
only land that could be bought—the half-marshland near the new
Ironworks.   There was digging and draining, dynamiting and
levelling.   Streets, houses, pubs, the cattle market, the first school,
the first chapels.   It was as if the heart of Old Odborough, swelling and bursting from its breast, had detached itself and gone
rolling down the hill, over the level-crossing to settle in the New
Town.

Tommy Dale's father was among the first to realise what was
happening.   From the level-crossing he saw the road run through

the still empty fields to the new houses midway between there and the Ironworks.   He saw the Cattle Market and *The Crown Hotel* take their places proud as pew-holders, beside the rectangular green that lay between Victoria Street and Albert Road.   He saw the new emporium of Happy Homes Ltd. facing them from the other side of the Green.   At the T-junction of Westmorland Road with Trafalgar Road the Bible Christians had begun to build their chapel, and Cumberland Road was the site for the Wesleyans, and, at the gas-works end, that for the Roman Catholics.   The private railway line to the furnaces passed close by between marsh and houses : if there were to be another Odborough station it might very well be there.   The, as yet, unbuilt-on land ran in a straight line over dead flat fields from the railway crossing to the Green; if there were to be trams, where could you find a more likely route ?   The Green, as Absalom Dale saw it, was the obvious civic centre of the new town.   He there-fore persuaded his firm to leave Old Odborough and open new premises midway between *The Crown* and the Cattle Mart—a long double-fronted shop with warehouse behind and living accommodation above.

For some years the town grew around him.   The fields between the Green and the Ironworks began to disappear, as the streets overstepped them on one side, and the grey dune of the slag-bank drifted over them on the other.   The shop prospered.   The Green assumed its right of assembly place.   The fairs came there and *Maria Marten*.   The club walks began there, and the Bible Christians held their first big mission in a tent on the grass.   On summer Saturdays wrestling matches were held, and brass-putting, and young men and girls met there, outside the Cattle Mart, on Hiring Days.

But the fourth side of the Green remained a waste lot.   The Town Hall, which old Mr Dale had envisaged, did not appear.   For there was a change coming over Odborough.   The excite-ment of its beginnings and growth had not yet died away, but now it was more aware of itself, and more aware, too, of the world outside.   What had once been a lost heath and haws now pro-claimed itself as a rightful part of the British Empire and not even

Livingstone, at the Victoria Falls, had made a greater discovery than this. The eyes of these new citizens of no mean city began to lift themselves above the marsh and the mines and the slag-bank to where, a quarter of a mile away, rose the nearest hill. It was the highest of the glacial drumlins, facing Old Odborough across the little valley in which lay the railway station, and part of it was already reserved as the site of St Kentigern's Church and the new graveyard. But a quarter of a mile seemed a long way from the packed and practical streets. The Council hesitated.

Then, suddenly, the railway company built a bridge, and built it, moreover, not on the site of the level-crossing but on the other end of the station, taking advantage of the rise of the hill. All at once the town was thrown on the wrong foot. The lane from *The Crown* Green which was to have been a broad, tram-thronged thoroughfare, now led nowhere. Instead, the lower slopes of St Kentigern's Hill became the one inevitable route for everyone entering or leaving New Town. The Council's mind was made up for it. Where the road descended to the new bridge they levelled and terraced the side of the hill, laid down a Square, and built the Town Hall. High above all the roofs and chimneys, the Town Clock displayed itself, proud as the Prince Consort. Opposite came the three banks, and on the third side of the Square, *The Prince of Wales Hotel*. And in the middle, with magnanimous remembrance of Her Majesty's other subjects, was placed the Queen Victoria ornamental horse-trough, where four iron lions spewed water into four stone basins.

At first the change meant little to Absalom Dale. The town was already beginning to divide itself into class-zones, and this new area had the look of the middle-class or, in a word just coming into use, of the residential. St Kentigern's Terrace, which joined the Square to the old, only half-built-up Rotting Road, was a street of bow-windows, each with its own carpet square of garden walled off from the pavement. The trade of the town still remained centred round the Green.

But as the century moved onwards, so the life and business of the town turned its back on the slag-banks and moved uphill. A Saturday Market was established in the hall beneath the Town

Clock. The Co-operative Society opened its stores at the top end of Waterloo Street, the farthest from the furnaces. One by one the bow-windows of St Kentigern's Terrace were converted into shop-fronts. The once-prosperous shops of Westmorland Road moved to new premises, or declined to pot-shops and penny sweet-shops and shops that sold glasses of herb beer and horehound.

Absalom Dale saw it and did not understand, but his son, young Tommy, did. He saw, but he did not worry, for he had now built up a solid-as-mahogany connection among the farmers and country gentlemen, and he supplied, wholesale, every little grocer's and confectioner's shop in every village for twenty miles around. He had three horse-vans and later, three motor-vans going out into the country every day. So that now, on this New Year's just-after-Eve, the shop remains secure and prosperous in a half-derelict square. The premises of Happy Homes Ltd. have declined through half-a-dozen bankrupted haberdashery and remnant stores into the whist-and-tattle rooms of the Old Age Pensioners, the plate-glass painted green for privacy. All the other shops are closed, and many demolished or condemned. Half the Green is enclosed as allotments—the lamplight hanging skeins of tinsel along the tin sheeting and old iron bedsteads which make up the fencing. Only *The Crown Hotel*, the Auction Mart, and A. Dale and Son (late Cheap and Best) retain the respectability of new paint and mortar.

Tommy Dale takes a final look out of his window. The Market Clock—though he cannot hear it—strikes one. He shoots the bolt on the Old Year and goes to bed.

.   .   .

You don't need to go far to look for spring, even on the second of January. The sun is looking for it, too. The sun is sharp and inquisitive, bending low, peeping under branch and blade, under shelf and ledge. The sun is seeing more of the world than it does in the high-and-mighty days of summer. It has been a cold, raw night and there is still rime lying on the shadow-side of hedge and vale, so that when, for a moment or two, the sun goes behind a cloud, the shadows are brighter than the ground which was sun-lit before.

At the corner where Rotting Road enters Furnace Road, and the Jubilee Road from the Market Square meets both of them, stands the Tin Tabernacle. It was built many years ago by the Welsh Calvinistic Methodists out of wood and corrugated iron. As a boy, I long believed that Calvinism was etymologically related to galvanised iron. But, for all its ramshackleness, it is unmistakably ecclesiastical. There is a steep tin roof and a porch, facing towards the Ironworks, and the windows are pointed like Early English lancets, cut straight out of the iron walls as if with an acetylene fret-saw, and filled with the frosted glass you find in bathrooms. Over the porch is a little gable-light in the form of a six-pointed star with red-and-green glass, which, on a Sunday night, shines down Furnace Road like a huge, genial Christmas-tree decoration.

Here the Welshmen worshipped in their own language and their own tunes. Many a boy, born in Odborough, could sing *Cwm Rhondda* as well as his father. Jack Edwards learnt to sing here, and for years the Male Voice Choir, the Mixed, the Working Men's, and even the Amateur Operatic Society, laid its foundations on a quartette of Welsh basses.

('It's the rock,' says Christopher Crackenthwaite. 'It's something that comes out of the rock, into the food and the water—that is what makes basses. You never get it in flat country. Whoever heard of a decent Male Voice Choir in a spot like Bedford?')

The Welsh died out. The iron rusted, the windows were broken, and the two-yard-wide garden which surrounded the chapel became waist-high in weed. The Brethren took over the building—(there is a notice outside:

> Every Sunday
> Breaking of Bread
> 2.30),

and have repaired the windows and painted the walls in dark plum red. On Tuesday evening the youth Orchestra practises there—though the Brethren, believing that there will be no instrumental music in heaven, insist on singing unaccompanied. And when—as happens about twice a year—a roof falls in or a wall falls out at the Rotting Road School, then the little hall becomes an emergency classroom.

Now, however, it is empty and closed. The back-porch juts out like a transept, its roof pricked and perky. The corrugations of the metal, emphasised by the shine and shadow of the sun, stripe the walls with verticles. It is a gothic fancy in metal, a biscuit-tin model of Milan Cathedral.

On its south side an old hedge divides it from the first open field on the fringe of the town. From this point there is not a brick between you and the Isle of Man. The wintering redwing that are feeding in the wet field—gregarious thrushes with surprised yellow eyebrows and underwings that look bloody as from a wound—could fly back home to Norway without even having to cross a single road. The hedge has stood there longer, even, than the chapel—alternate layers of sods and cobbles, the broken ends of slates left over from building, or fragments of limestone, or even knobs and crumbles of slag embedded in the clay. Stone and sod have so knitted together that the hedge looks like a slant of fell-side with crag breaking through the soil. The cobbles take the full glare of the low sun and the not-yet-melted hoar frost in the crevices glints like quartz.

The thorns which run along the top of this dyke have not been trimmed for years. Already they have become not so much a hedge as a row of stunted trees. Each rises on its black trunk and creaks round the chapel, like an umbrella blown inside out. A tatter of black leaves still adheres to the finger-tips of the branches, yet along the twists of the wood there are everywhere tight warts and pimples of bud. The ashes, mingled with the thorn, kick into the air their long, clean colt's legs, each with a black hoof at the end. The elders, too, are clean, being bent and brown and brittle as if made of pipe-clay. Even a hazel appears here and there, its inch-long catkins a stiff bright green. While the catkins of the one decrepit alder—its top snapped off for a bonfire—are purple and bunched and curved like a bird's claws.

None of these, however, is exclusive to spring. Buds and cat-kins belong as much to autumn, and are a commonplace of October in any country lane.   Yet the eye knows for certain that the year is new, that something has changed since last it looked at this spot, three or four weeks ago.   It is not easy to be sure what this can be.   The hedge-bank looks fresher, brighter—but this might just be the effect of the sun.   It looks cleaner—but this might be the effect of last week's rain.   It looks greener, too —but that is due, not so much to the coming of greenness, but to the tearing away of the old year's rag-mat of brown and black and yellow.

Yet this is not all : for along the hedge-top in among the trunks of the thorn, and up and down the sods among the stones, there is a hint and frill of leaves no bigger than confetti, scattered in the black soil.   A month or two may reveal them as belonging to a score of species : goosegrass, speedwell, celandine, moschatel.   But now they are still anonymous, still indistinguishable each from the other, yet as intent and purposeful as a hatching of insects creeping out of their cracks in the early sun.

Here and there is a recognisable plant : chickweed, as green as Ireland, with its small, mean, jealous eyes, that will never shut so long as there is a peep of light; ivy-leaved toadflax with its little purple snapdragons draping itself over the lumps of slag as if it were in the window-box or greenhouse from which it originally came.   And there are also the red dead-nettle, the daisy, common groundsel, and even a dandelion.   But these are just flowers that don't know what time of year it is.

Nevertheless, the real spring flower, the first flower of the front-end, is already in bloom.   Move up Jubilee Hill, from the chapel of the Brethren to the church of the Establishment, and you will find a curiously prolific and persistent weed.   It spreads all over the bank that divides the drive from the vicarage garden in among the trees, right up the slope towards the graveyard—nearly a quarter of an acre of it.   Digging and burning has not the slightest effect on it, for below the surface is an entanglement of roots, tough as barbed wire.   God knows how long it has been there. Church people know it as a familiar nuisance.   Those who visit the churchyard only for funerals and Armistice Day processions notice it without knowing they have done so, and carry its green as part of the image of corruption and decay. Thousands of mourners, passing up the drive, have had their attention diverted for one second to its rankness—a sprawl not of the resurrection but of cold endurance. Those who return to Odborough after an absence of many years are astonished to recognise the weed, so long forgotten, growing unchanged in a town of changed faces.

Few people have ever seen it in flower. All they have seen is the wilderness of leaves—leaves very like those of colt's-foot, but of a brighter green; flat, heart-shaped leaves, the size of pancakes, that curl at the edges and are veined, puckered, and crinkled like human skin. Yet there *is* a flower for those who know where and when to look for it: a tallish spike bearing a dozen flower-heads, each surprisingly like mauve colt's-foot heads, and the whole very like butterbur, or wild rhubarb. It is a stiff unprepossessing bloom, somewhat resembling those brushes which are used to clean lavatory bowls. Yet, gathered, it has a faint honey fragrance, unique among the winter flowers, because of which, no doubt, some vicar's wife planted it years ago.

The present vicar hates the plant. He has seen the flowers and has recognised them for what they are—winter heliotrope, *Petasites fragrans*—but he feels that it makes the neighbourhood of the church-porch look too much like a rubbish-heap. Nothing he can do seems to discourage it—nothing short of digging a six-foot trench and filling it with solid concrete. He has nightmares in which the weed seems to be the only green thing left in a hydrogen-bombed world—persistent, flourishing, and drawing a new vitality from the radio-active air.

At this very moment he is walking among the weed, though without thinking of it. He is looking for something else. Here, in the vicarage garden, planted when shade was a luxury, the hoar-frost still lies on much of the lawn, and on the leaves of the winter heliotrope under the trees. On this northern slope of the hill, tilted away from the sun, the day is grey-green, with the dim sheen of a mistletoe berry. Lawn, evergreens, and gravel are furred like a liverish tongue, and the whole garden looks crumbly and soluble, as if it were made of a damp grey-green chemical substance, salt with no savour. Canon Olds glances round, searching. He does not need to wait for long, for suddenly a bird flies out of the bushes almost to his feet—a grey-green bird, seeming to be made, like everything else, out of the same salty substance; or maybe a bird of stone on which the hoar-frost had formed overnight.

From its shape it is unmistakably robin. The wings are of the normal robin colour, and so, too, is the crown of the head, and there is a very faint pinkness, of about the size of a sixpence, on either side of the beak. Elsewhere—forehead, breast, belly, legs, and under-tail—all is a hoary off-grey, which when the bird moves into the light becomes a pearly off-white.

It is, in fact, an albino, a half-white robin, which was hatched out in the vicarage garden during the last spring, at the same time as a white, or pied, blackbird. For months, now, Canon Olds has been feeding it, so that it comes regularly to the door, obviously quite unaware of its oddness, and with no fears of the predicament which may be ahead of it. But the Vicar is aware of it, for he knows how important is the red breast in the life of a robin. Indeed, since robins will react to a red rag of the right size as if it were another robin, how will they react to this robin, this plaster model of its kind? Will they recognise it as a robin at all? Will it be able to claim and hold its territory without the bluffing and boasting of the red signal? Will it be able to find a mate? Perhaps some colour-blind cock or hen will accept it. Or perhaps it will be seen as a robin only in the eyes of man, as the madman, the saint, and the poet are seen as man only in the eyes of God.

In any case, thinks Canon Olds, what an obvious and apposite symbol for the poet is this little singer, despised and rejected of birds, this freak and treasure, this rarity and epitome, this less than and more than a robin.

The bird hunches its neck, looking up sideways, alert for crumbs. Suddenly, as if tired of waiting, it darts to the border, and catches a worm by the tail, and tugs at it as if it were six inches of elastic. In the shadows it no longer looks different from

any other robin, and goes on tugging and jerking, far n
concerned to be an ordinary bird than to provide an excuse for a
poem or a platitude.

.   .   .

The weather has changed as quick as the twist of a tap. The
first Ironworks buzzer wakes me at five-thirty—a long dinosaur
moo, followed by two short snorts—and immediately I feel that
the world has broken into a hot sweat. I put a hand out of bed
and find that the wall is as wet as a fishmonger's marble slab. So
is the woodwork of my bed, and, indeed, everything of metal or
stone which is within touchable distance. The room is steaming
like a greenhouse, and glass, wood, and iron are slobbery with
water. My head, too, feels like a washtub with suddy vapour
oozing from my eyes. The meteorologists will say that a warm,
damp airstream arriving suddenly from the Atlantic precipitated
its moisture on every surface that was still cold with the frost.
For myself, it will be said that I have a cold in the head and must
stay in bed.

But this does not mean that I am absent from the life of the
town. For this life is like an enormous hurdy-gurdy, every wheel
cogged to another wheel, so that, merely from the sounds which
reach my bedroom window in St Kentigern's Terrace, I can read
nearly all the turnings and whirligigging of the whole contraption.

After the Ironworks buzzer there is half an hour's pause. The
men are tying their bootlaces, picking up their bait-tins, swilling
down hot tea and puffed or powdered or shredded maize or oats
or grass-seed. (' It's a caution when you have to go out to work
on nubbut a couple of fire-lighters,' says Chunker Wilson.)

Then comes a trickle of footsteps, a rippling river of rolling
pebbles, gathering its tributaries from back and side street. The
waters pass by and dry up. Then the mail train, at the station,
applying its brakes; the post-office van bringing the letters, the
boys delivering the morning papers, each letter-box clattering.
Footsteps again—the high heels of girl assistants at the early-
opening shops. St Kentigern's Communion bell. Children's
voices, the scratch and scamper of buses. Bleat of sheep and bark

c

ction Mart Day—I had forgotten.   The farmers
wn.

great big silly-looking begger.   Aren't you dead
greeting of pleasure and affection.

he Prince of Wales I hear the voices of boys waiting
o whack the cows all the way down Albert Road to
the Auction on *The Crown* Green.   The Market Clock strikes
nine, but they take no notice.

The first shopping cars.   And now to the growing but barely
perceptible murmur of the morning the neighbours add each his
trade-mark tune or tinkle.   Old Mr Sprout, the greengrocer,
greets the street with a voice that for fifty Harvest Festivals has
hosannahed the roof off the Bible Christian Chapel.   The young
manager at the ironmonger's slaps every lady's bicycle within
reach into a giggle of bells and rivets.   Christopher Crackenthwaite condescends to the day like a tuba-player being introduced
to the new cornet.

' A large morning, Mr Wilson,' he says magnanimously.

' You've got your share of it, so what are you fratching about?'
Chunker replies.

The hours gossip past till the Market Clock strikes twelve.
Buzzers bray, buses rev up, school unbuckles its satchel, and all
along the street the Yale locks snap the shops into the silence of
lunch-time.

There is nothing mechanical or impersonal about this rhythm.
Instead, there is a continual approach and meeting, an inter-
patterning and overlapping of individual lives, a counterpointing
of one man's day with the days of other men.   The worsteds of a
thousand separate homes are woven together.

We are all of us creatures of rhythm.   We gear our waking
and sleeping to the rising and setting of the sun, and our blood
retains the heat as well as the salt of the sea from which we come.

Nor is it merely the sun that dictates the rhythms by which we
order our lives.   We create our own little solar systems in home
and family.   Life circles round life, swerves out on its orbit,
moves from opposition to conjunction.   The kettle is put on to
boil when the train whistles in the cutting; a dog sniffs at the door

when the wireless is switched off after the News; Tommy Dale shuts shop when the foreman from the quarry walks into *The Crown* for his on-the-way-home pint.

Habit is as necessary as the cogs in a clock. Habit does half our life's work for us; without it, half would not be done. When the elder Miss Snoot comes downstairs on a winter morning she empties the tepid water of her hot-water bottle into a cyclamen pot and her bowls of bulbs. Buy her an electric blanket and her plants will die of drought. Every Sunday evening, on her way to the Spiritualist Room, Mrs Makeweight posts a letter to her married daughter in Accrington. When at Christmas, the time of collection is altered, she cannot go to the service. For my own part, all my poems have to be written on the backs of letters— typed letters on good opaque paper. If, when a poem wants to be written I can find no letter to write on the back of, then the poem may be lost or forgotten. Other kinds of paper will not do —notepaper, foolscap, exercise-books, or the old ledger in which I am writing now. I know quite well that with these I shall not be able to start—the words will not come. So I must search hastily through drawerfuls of old letters, hoping that the original impulse will not have subsided by the time I find what I need.

Habit is also a drug, an anaesthetic, sending us sleep-walking through the day; with wide unseeing eyes we grope along the lobbies of the morning, snoring as we walk. The postman knocks at the door.

' Good morning. Not much this morning.'

' Good day,' we snore back. ' Thank you and good day.'

Snoring through this good day we grope back in the mirk of habit, never tasting the goodness, never stopping to claim from the starlings our part of this proud-as-chimney-pot morning.

Yet for the old, for the ill and bewildered, habit is the one valve that keeps the blood still moving in the veins. At half-past seven every evening, whatever he may be doing and in whatever company, old Mr Postlethwaite walks into the kitchen, takes off his collar and tie, and has a good wash at the sink. Sixty years ago, coming home from his chemist's shop, he had washed before supper at just that time. Now with the shop sold out to the

multiples and the cardboard advertisements propped in front of
the bedroom fireplaces to keep out the draught, the habit ticks on.
On his eightieth birthday his grandchildren promised him a first-
class dinner at *The Prince of Wales* to family and neighbours—
cars, carnations, and a chemist's carboy filled with rum-and-
orange to drink his health. But he would not miss his wash.

Throughout our working and idling lives we move in a re-
current and predictable climate of habit : of the habit of other
people, people we know, people we do not know, people we have
never seen.

Johnnie Moss, the newsagent, Violet's uncle, collects the
morning papers off the mail and leaves a copy of the *Manchester
Guardian* with the porter, who gives it to the clerk of the Ironworks, arriving by the seven-thirty train, who takes it to the bus-
stop and passes it to Mr McIntosh, who, in fact, has paid for it.
Mr McIntosh likes to read it in the bus. In the privacy of his
laboratory, however, he prefers to read the *Daily Mirror,* which
he has not paid for, while the clerk, who *has* paid for it, dreams
over the Situations Vacant column of the *Guardian.* When Mrs
Scrubbit, the cleaner, comes in at six o'clock, the *Mirror* is taken
for supper-time reading, but the *Guardian* goes to lay the office
fire. At seven o'clock each morning, while the new day's edition
waits in the station ticket-room, yesterday's news smokes upwards
to mingle in the smother from the furnace stacks.

Easily, inevitably, one life is knitted into another. Each one
lives in a rhythm drummed out by the sun and the seasons, but
against this is a complex counter-rhythm of minor accents and
syncopations, in which every beat has a human hand behind it
and every voice is familiar and recognisable. Each life becomes
part of the background, part of the environment of the others. It
is not a matter of choice or decision, nor of common aims, nor
hopes, nor opinions. There may be as many disagreements as
there are men; there may be—there certainly is—pettiness,
jealousy, and spite. Yet for the most part, each of us learns to
accept the others as belonging to that one rhythm, that improvised,
haphazard, conductorless, trumpeting town band in which he
himself has his few notes to play.

The music we produce may be insignificant, out of date, and naïve. It has neither the power nor the promise to make a big noise in the world. It cannot compete with the ordered symphonies of the cities, the choral march of a million strangers caught in a rhythm from which they can never break free. But at least it gives each one of us a chance to blow his own penny whistle, and to learn to listen to the others. And, sometimes, for a moment, it may allow him to have the tune to himself.

.   .   .

P.C. Goosefoot gazes across the Market Square with satisfaction. It is a quarter to nine on a pouring wet evening of late January. The Square is practically empty. The few youths standing in the doorways and under the Market Arch protrude their heads every now and then into the rain till they seem to spout like gargoyles. Chuck a drunk out of *The Prince of Wales* on a night like this, and in fifteen seconds the rain would swill him sober.

P.C. Goosefoot clasps his hands behind his back, flaps round on his flipper-like feet with the confidence of a performing seal, and splashes into the Jubilee Road. This is the sort of night he is glad to be a policeman. No brawls, no fireworks, not even Daphne Huggins in a squeal of evasion down the back streets. The rain does not bother him at all. He can be happy out of doors in any weather, and he feels nothing but gratitude to a calling which gives him his legitimate, and even respectable, reason for walking the streets, the allotments, the footpaths, and the railway sidings at noon, at night, and in the empty hours of the morning.

It is only the policeman's petty duties which irritate him—such as checking dog licences or arresting murderers. Luckily there is not much likelihood of any such tonight. For he believes in going about his job calmly and quietly, interfering with no one, doing no one any harm. He has an intuitive foreknowledge of trouble in any part of the town, and takes care to keep as far as possible from it. When a shop is burgled or a girl is thrown into the bushes, not even the culprit has a better alibi than Constable Goosefoot.

He glances at the Town Clock—time is nicely in hand. A Nonconformist ground-landlord has laid down in the leases that no licensed premises shall be opened in what was formerly her property, so that except for *The Prince of Wales* and the Working Men's, all the pubs of Odborough are to be found far away on the Ironworks side of Cumberland Road, between the Wesleyan Chapel and the slag-bank. This means that if the Constable regulates his walk with care he can be well out of reach or hearing of any pub just about closing-time.

Not that P.C. Goosefoot objects to late-night work. None but the sparrows knows better than he how to make himself snug of a winter's night. There is the west porch of the Tin Tabernacle, looking towards the lights of the mines—which is capital for a night with an east wind. There is the old entry at the bottom of Trafalgar Road, a tunnel between two parlours, running from front street to back—which is a splendid place to shelter from a storm, provided you don't choose a time when someone is using it for another purpose. There are nooks and crannies, school porches, the angles of walls, gateways, and gardens, where a man of a philosophical turn of mind can make himself cosy and content, interpreting the morse flickers of street-lamp and bedroom light.

He turns from the Square to the comparative darkness of Jubilee Road.

' Good evening, Officer '—it is Christopher Crackenthwaite on his way to the Working Men's. The formal mode of address is reserved for his familiars—if he were introduced to the Duke of Edinburgh he would at once call him ' Phil '.

' Salubrious evening.'

P.C. Goosefoot does not reply. There is, indeed, no reason for him to reply, for with a duck-shuffle of coat-tail and a seal-like flip of hands he has invented his own manner of repartee, and out of his very silence has made himself the reputation of a wit.

He moves now to the unlit side of the road, by the railings which divide it from the Jubilee Pleasure Ground. Here he is on the edge of the dark that stretches over field and dune and derelict minings across the Irish Sea and the North Channel until, a

thousand miles out in the Atlantic, it catches up with the sunset. You can sense how, until almost the beginning of this
century, the dark crept like a thief right to the outermost house of
every town and village of Europe. In the moon's last quarter
every cluster of houses was barricaded from the rest of the world
by the unchinked blackness of night.

The constable's feet play noisy ducks and drakes in a puddle.
He is aware of a commotion in the gooseberry bushes just inside
the railways—there is, as he has taken care not to know, a way of
squeezing through the railings between the Pleasure Ground and
the Tin Tabernacle. Quickly he averts his eyes and moves across
the road, noticing how the untended privets, grown almost to
trees, strain and sway like seaweed in the tide. Beyond the allotments, in Rotting Road, Johnnie Dodder's bedroom light is burning as usual. This is the kind of night on which he likes to lean
out of his window in the dark shouting at the passers-by:

' Away off home, you silly beggar. What you want out on a
night like this?' Or sometimes, with a sudden sharpness : ' Now
then. Less of that.'

Couples who are not aware of the trick jump guiltily apart, but
Constable Goosefoot always has the kindness to stare ostentatiously
up and down the street as if he had no idea where the voice was
coming from.

He moves on past Rotting Road School. The rain falls now
dead straight, now slantingly, like a shining bead curtain blown
about in the wind. For a second or two it eases off, making a
little cone of drizzle around the policeman, while elsewhere the
water splashes in bucketfuls, swilling all the walls and gutters of
the town. The lights are on in the school—dressmaking class,
woodwork, and cookery. Constable Goosefoot could name them
all as he goes about his duty, night by night, schoolroom, clubroom, and huts with their rows of lighted windows among the
playground sycamores : the night-classes, the Scouts, the opera
practice, the Chess club, the Gramophone Society, the Town's-
women's Guild, the Keep-fit, and the Old Age Pensioners. The
playground, under the swirl of rain and lamplight, is a clutter of
jerry and makeshift : old air-raid shelters adapted as storerooms,

old air-raid shelters left as shelters, new pre-fab classrooms, wooden buttresses to keep old walls from falling, new walls where old ones have already fallen. Yet in this water-logged dusk the schools look much as they have done for sixty years. The two-light windows raise pointed eyebrows, and the steep-pitched roof, gable-ends, ventilators, and bell-tower spike upwards into the darkness, or catch pink gleams from the furnace. More than ever, in this weather, they look like almshouses where a basinful of thin learning is ladled out to Oliver Twists who will never ask for more. The constable passes *The Jubilee Jug* and moves into the aura of the first fish-and-chip shop, where the rain feels warmer, and the air is cosy with the purring of vinegar. He turns into Trafalgar Road, past Ma Gawthwaite's herb-beer shop, where for three-pence you can get a glass of cold horehound, thick and black as tar, and tasting of the dockens and waterweeds of every ditch between the Town Tip and the Ironworks Reservoir. The few other shops are now closed. Passing Tyson's Fresh Tripe, Constable Goosefoot remembers that more than once Mr Tyson has complained about nuisances in the doorway. He therefore switches on his electric torch to reveal Daphne Huggins tight in the arms of Tyson's errand boy. Too startled to switch off, the constable stands for a moment like a burglar holding a spotlight to a safe. The two take not the slightest notice.

' No consideration for a policeman's feelings,' he says to himself as he moves away.

Past the Bible Christian Chapel; past ' The Brew ', or Employment Exchange. No more shops; the street dark and conspiratorial. On to the Goose Green at the end of the street below the slag-bank. Here, on a scuffle of grass, staked with poles for clothes-lines, half a dozen geese spend the days of summer, parading like cadets, or chivvying bicycles and dogs. There's not a farmer in the district can be sure of his poultry, and the police are continuously getting calls about stolen chickens and turkeys. Yet these geese wander freely about this poorer part of the town protected by the unclosing eyes of the neighbours.

Constable Goosefoot crosses the Green into Marsh Edge Street —the almost derelict street that runs along the foot of the slag-bank joining the broken-down ends of Furnace Road, Trafalgar Road, Waterloo Street, and Albert Road. The ends—or, rather, beginnings. For here in this rubble of half-demolished or decaying houses, of collapsed inns haunted by the suicide of a licence, of rotting yards and warehouses crammed with scrap-iron, cement, steam-rollers, and old cars—here was the cradle of the town. Here were born the great-grandfathers of the families who made Odborough—the Threlkelds and Broughams, the Postlethwaites and Snoots and Nicholsons. The rain batters against the rake-end of the slag-bank, its outline discernible only because of the continual glow from the furnace that hangs over this lower part of the town. At the side of the road the gas-lamps—for electricity has not reached Marsh Edge Road—faintly illumine the gulleys of the slag, where rain runnels down in little flood-becks and forces. The rain collects around the lamp-post—each pool carrying a dim green scum of gaslight, out of which cobbles of slag protrude.

At this point, if it were daylight, the constable could have seen seven pubs—*The Furnace Arms, The Iron Man, The Miner's Arms, The Whippet, The White Mouse, The Wicked Lord,* and *The Sailor,* some of them already in ruins, clustered together on the edge of the teetotal terraces. He passes the scrap-house that was once *The Whippet* and turns into the bottom of Waterloo Street. Now he is right among the dead Victorian tenements, their window sockets emptied, their flesh stripped to the rafters. He starts, like a ghost in a graveyard, staring along the years to where electricity comes in at Westmorland Road, and the chain-shops and the Co-operative keep their window lights on, and high above them all, half a mile away, the Town Clock marks its twentieth-century time.

He walks between still-occupied houses and among tiny shops where widows stock lemonade, and young wives sell ice-cream, tinned soups, and firewood while their husbands are out at work.. These part-time shops, taken on to pay the rent or because the woman is bored, were the beginnings of the retail fortunes of the town. Here hung the hams and sides of bacon, with black puddings, sacks of flour and dried peas, rice, oatmeal, yeast, and

Yorkshire Relish.   Tatters and chippings of their former prosperity are still glued to the window panes:

RY'S   C C A

and   M Z W TEE   TE

And here and there, behind counters or at the back of the shelves,
lie old advertisement cards—VIROL and SWAN VESTAS and the
fat-faced little Lord Fauntleroy, blowing his bubbles of Pear's
Soap.   As business moved towards the new centre of the town,
these little shops lived on through the chronic consumption of
bankruptcy.   But the case, now, is different.   Here a new kind
of retail business has arisen, which thrives on the new spending-
power of the two—or three—wage-packet homes of the workers.
These shops do not pretend to the status of the Edwardian Family
Grocer or Italian Warehousemen, who liked to supply enough
food at one selling to stock a household of twelve for a month.
Instead they cater for the poppers-out, the mothers with just a
minute to spare, the wives who want something tasty for tea.
Some of them act as agents for the larger greengrocers and confectioners, selling tomatoes, bread, and cakes on commission.
Others rely on pre-fabricated food—meat-pies in cellophane, swiss
rolls in tin-foil, sausages in tomato, potted salmon, tinned carrots,
tinned pineapple, potato crisps, pork and beans, salad cream, red
pickled cabbage, bottled blackcurrant juice, and non-alcoholic
cider.   Where the term ' Mixed Business ' used to bring an image
of a dark, dusky shop in a muddle of turnips, humbugs, and hair-
grips, it means today, more often, a neat little shop blooming like
a florist's in all the colours of the fifty-seven varieties.

There are a few men, as usual, in the doorway of Chunker
Wilson's billiard saloon—one of them, as P.C. Goosefoot is well
aware, an unofficial bookie's agent.

' Bonny night for the geese,' he says, as the constable walks past
on the other side.

But the latter does not hear him.   Nor is he concerned, tonight,
to prevent the breaking of the betting laws.   Instead, he is
absorbed in the contemplation of the shops.   He can do this with

more ease, since it is not his duty on this beat to try the doors to see if they are safely locked up for the night. And sure enough, if anyone does leave a shop unsecured, it will be someone who lives on the far side of Old Odborough or someone who has to be searched for among the houses of a dozen friends and neighbours. Tonight, however, he need do no more than enjoy the sight of the darkened windows in the pouring rain, looking like spectacles with no eyes behind them. Wilson's, Makeweight's, Cohen late Snoot, Crackenthwaite's showroom, Old Postlethwaite's now Cash Chemists, The Maypole, The Meadow, The Co-op, Goodness Grocers (Goodness Agencies:

> Bunn's Bread
> Lyon's Cakes
> Palethorpe's sausages
> Furness Steam Laundry).

Shift them about, and how different his beat would be. It would be like shuffling the books of the Bible, like putting Friday before Tuesday, like changing half-day closing. For did not the position of these shops, and their character, go towards making the basic common experience of everyone who belonged to the town? The children learned their first knowledge of the worldly world precisely from those shops—the world of money, and merchandise, of buying and selling. Of what enormous significance to the child might not be the fact that he had to pass the ironmonger's to get to the toy shop, or that he got his ice-cream from the same shop as the newspapers, or that the one place where he could buy the lemonade that he liked best was over the Bridge and away up the hill of Old Odborough. As for those who were children fifty years ago, had not Mr Snoot given to calico and muslin a serious dignity, and Mr Dale to washing soda a straight-batted Evangelical honesty, that neither hire-purchase nor processed packing could ever entirely remove? There are some shopkeepers who behave as if they made the town, and P.C. Goosefoot sometimes thinks they are right.

.   .   .

But everyone else is certain they are wrong.   Once, when I was at school, the class was asked to give an example of a hypocrite, and the son of the Methodist minister suggested a shopkeeper.

' He buys at one price,' he explained, ' and sells at another.'

The idea stung me like a nettle, for my father was a shop-keeper, and until then I had always felt rather proud of his position among the tradespeople, and proud, too, of being able to live behind the shop in St Kentigern's Terrace, the hub of the town.   But now I realised that it was not everyone who gave to the shopkeeper the respect to which he still felt he was entitled. I became aware that the word ' bourgeois '—at that time just coming into the popular vocabulary—applied with extraordinary etymological aptness to the owner of a one-man shop.   Nor indeed was ' bourgeois ' the worst.   More often it was ' petty bourgeois ', the little townsman, the small capitalist, the mean, insignificant, paltry money-grubber and property-owner.   The petty bourgeois produced nothing.   He contributed nothing in service or in ideas.   He was answerable to no employer or institution.   He was parasitic on industry, was out only for what he could get, had no concern for the welfare of society, was selfish, narrow-minded, irresponsible, and reactionary.   That is how we were taught to think of the shopkeeper in the 1920s.

It took me a long time to recognise the naïveté of this attitude. But gradually I came to understand that, far from living on the labour of others, my father had exacted from himself a standard of industriousness such as no employer would have dared to demand. I realised, too, that the distribution of trousers is at least as essential to the community as the work of the miner or the engine driver.

So that I began to see my father's business within the perspec-tive of the town's history.   I pictured the sales of fifty years arranging themselves as in a haberdasher's ballet.   I saw the purchases passing over the counter—small parcels in green or mauve ' cap ' paper, large ones in brown paper, hats and gloves in bags.   I followed the tracks they made from the shop, along the street, upstairs into bedrooms and underground into the mines; or over the Railway Bridge, past the Police Station, and out to the villages and the farms among the hills.   I watched them all

in their appointed places, busy about their appointed tasks, as if
worn by five generations of invisible men : butterfly collars sitting
stiffly in the Baptist Chapel; Edwardian striped blazers leaning
over the rails of the cricket pavilion; vests and drawers at high tide
left lying on Odborough Rocks; grey kid gloves in payment for
mistletoe kisses; khaki handkerchiefs parcelled off to soldiers;
knickerbockers, Oxford bags, plus-fours, and flannels. Yet, in
spite of all this, I could not quite understand my father's satisfaction in his shop; could not understand his care of every fitting;
could not understand from whence he derived that which in another calling would have been described as a ' sense of vocation '.

When my father started work in the 1890s the town was in its
first full urban prosperity, drawing wealth from one of the most
wonderful deposits of haematite iron ever discovered. Its social
hierarchy, however, was still largely rural. The town children
doffed their caps to the squires from the country as they drove by
in trap and gig. The shop assistants bowed to them, even when
they did not pay their bills. The very bosses at the mines
pretended to be country gentlemen and wore tweeds and judged
at the agricultural shows. In such a society, as in that of Jane
Austen's day, it would seem that tradesmen could find no honour-
able place.

But already it was beginning to change, and the status of the
tradesman changed with it. So that when my father was
apprenticed for seven years to Seth Slater, tailor and sub-
postmaster, it was with no thought of subjection in his mind. Mr
Slater was a strict Methodist, straight as pew-back in carriage and
character, and from him my father learned to approach business
with the same seriousness that was required by the Young Men's
Bible Class or the Christian Endeavour. For seriousness was not
yet out of fashion. A man could buy a paper with a title like
Great Thoughts without feeling any embarrassment. In the
shop, therefore, punctuality, patience, the acceptance of long
hours, the continual readiness to oblige—these became moral
virtues. To fail in any of them meant not just loss of business but
a loss of self-esteem.

In 1907 my father moved to the other side of the street and

opened up on his own.   By now the tradesman had gone up in the world and had begun to take part in the life of the town as councillor, magistrate, organiser, or committee man.   Pre-1914 industrial England still seemed as broad as the Bible, and the tradesman felt that he had his share in the glory of his country and the portly optimism of his King.   He no longer bowed low to his customers, but treated them with a new ease, a new equality, even, perhaps at times, with a certain condescension.

The pride in the standard of service remained, however, as I came to realise when my father died and for two months I had to be in charge of the shop.   I did so reluctantly, knowing very little about it, and feeling the strain on my limited physical powers. Yet as I began to learn my way about the shop, I realised the pleasure my father must have taken in his work—the satisfaction of giving value, of buying judiciously, of meeting a customer's needs.   I remembered how much he disliked having to sell imperfect goods during the War, and how he would sometimes refuse to let a regular customer buy an article he wanted, saying, frankly, that it was not worth the money.   I remembered, too, his genuine pleasure when he had been able to supply exactly what was required.

He would return to the kitchen behind the shop, tilting back his head and peering through the very bottom segment of his spectacles.

' I've just got two pound seventeen out of old so-and-so,' he'd say.

But his real pleasure was in the fact that he had pleased the customer; his real pride was a craftsman's pride in his job.   The shop was his own creation, as a picture is the artist's creation.   It was a projection of his own personality, and it was because of this that he took such enormous care in the polishing of counters and the dusting of shelves, and in the saving of space or the arrange-ment of stock.   More than once I have known him annoyed when a customer has bought an article from window or counter, so spoiling his design or colour scheme.   There was a pleasure to be gained from neatness and orderliness quite apart from its effect on sales.

Above all, I remember my father's reply to the traveller who called and asked to see the boss.

' I am my own boss,' he said.

He had disciplined his life for fifty years so that he could make that reply. He had worked ten and sometimes twelve hours a day, as a young man, Saturdays and Christmas Eve, had refused the offers of multiple firms, had run all the risks of the Depression and the two wars. And he had no doubt at all that it had been worth it.

For most men, I suppose, it would not have been worth it. They envisaged themselves more readily as the boss of someone else than as their own boss. Moreover, my father's independence during that time was always precarious, and perhaps, in terms of economics, it was an illusion. But, in terms of human enterprise it was not an illusion. In terms of human enterprise it was not a bad way of living, and society will be narrower in the future if it holds no chance for the man who is ready to take the risk. The man who wants to be his own boss.

Such men, however, are less likely to turn to the retail trade. For after the Depression the buying power moved from the farming families and the professional classes to the working-class. And the working-man prefers not the small one-man shop, but the larger, company-owned multiple store. It seems at first a curious contradiction of his natural sympathies to support the capitalist, dividend-paying, out-of-town firm as against the small personally known local trader. This is partly, no doubt, because these stores are better able to provide the cheap mass-produced article. But it is partly, I suspect, because of a resentment against that very independence which, however humbly, the private tradesman still enjoys. The manager of the multiple shop may earn in salary and commission a good deal more than the profits of the one-man shop, yet he is still an employee—in the eyes of the working-man he is one of them, while the private tradesman belongs with the bosses.

The one-man shop is becoming an anachronism, tending for the most part to serve what is known as ' the better-class trade '. In its place come the multiples, the co-operatives, the hire-purchase

firms, and those family businesses where, too often, everyone toils
for twenty years without rest and without holiday, in order, at the
end, to retire to a bungalow in the next village.   The standardis-
ation of goods makes it easier for the man with no knowledge of
the trade to buy a business and make a success of it.   The old
craftsman-tradesman, working on his own without assistants and
without outside capital, is on his way out.   And with him will go
some of that quiet laughter and cheerful independence which
have been heard up and down the shops of England since the time
of *The Shoemaker's Holiday.*

February

OR NEARLY a week the fist of the frost has held tight to the land. There have been brilliant Candlemas days when the tiles seemed to skip under the whip of the cold. There have been opaque days, when the sky was heaped and blizzarded with snow, and yet the snow did not fall. Only occasional flakes came haphazardly down like white sifts of charred paper when a chimney is on fire. Everywhere else there was snow. Scotland was kilt-deep in it; it was up to the lorry-axles on Shap, up to the bus-steps in London. At Old Trafford it was wicket-high, and in Sussex it was up to the Downs. On the brown fells above the estuary there were chalkings of snow, streaks and hatchings and high-lights. But here all was bare.

Then yesterday morning the wind dodged into the south-west and thaw slithered across the land, and, suddenly, improbably, out of the thawing wind came the snow. It melted as it fell, but not as fast as it fell. Pavements and gutters were filled with cold tapioca pudding.

D   49

'This'll soon get away,' everyone said. 'It's wet as muck already. It'll turn to rain in no time.'

But in the evening, under the dark, the gulleys ceased to drip, the pudding took a crust, and everyone was saying, 'Shouldn't be surprised if it snowed again.'

Yet they *were* surprised. One is always surprised by snow. The streets themselves looked surprised, holding their breath in an anxious hush—a hush which is perhaps the strangest thing about the snow. As you look at the street, seeing movement and hearing none, you feel as if an unnatural deafness had come upon you. Your eyes and your ears do not co-ordinate; it is very much like the sensation of a fever. The chimneys are bewildered, the roofs, slippery and uncertain. Dormer windows prick up their ears like terriers. The birds flop in the snow, learning to ski.

But the snow itself is completely without surprise. I survey it from my bedroom window and everywhere it is quite at home. It lies on the slates, unmarked except by sparrows; it swells and balloons over the edge of the launders. The roofs have lost their straight-line geometry of slant and perpendicular. The chimneys, hung with white soot, jerk up from a Moscow of onion-domed attics. Starlings, blundering among the chimney-pots, precipitate small avalanches over their tails. Jackdaws, trying to settle on the watershed of a roof, find themselves top-heavy and fly away, clacking like nutcrackers. The sparrows alone, with their urchin adaptability, have found their snow legs, and know already that today the street-bottoms are as safe as the air and that they run no danger from dog or bicycle.

The 'lum hats' of the chimney-pots are padded with white felt on the one side. A three-inch ribbon of snow, sideways up, is balanced on the telephone wires until, now and then, a bird lets on them, and ten or twenty yards fall like droppings into the street. The spire of St Kentigern's, seen above the Banks, carries one elongated isosceles triangle of pure white from base to weathercock.

I push open my casement windows, making two carvings of snow tumble from the attic roof into the little balcony above the shop-window. The snow-plough has not yet been round, but already the street is trampled by the men going to work. No school-children so far, but I can hear the first faint scrapes and slushing of householders beginning to clean their pavements, and the sound is strange and hard to recognise in the almost silent air, seeming as if it came from a long distance, a country sound in the wrong place. Old Sprout, the greengrocer, banging the door behind him as he comes out of his shop, loosens half a cart-load of snow, which skids off his roof and pancakes on the pavement, missing his head by no more than a foot.

' Glory!' he says. ' Greenland's icy mountains.'

Half a dozen of Chris Crackenthwaite's apprentices pass down the street just as the girls begin to arrive at the Market Hall factory. At once there is a parabolic storm of snowballs. Headscarves, bootees, mackintoshes, and woollen gloves are whirled and scrimmaged together. The air glistens with screeching. Snowballs explode like white bombs on doors and lamp-posts. Girls, caught by the arm, have snow rubbed into their hair like salt into a herring. Three of them, catching a youth who is trying to push a bicycle through a snow-drift, tip him into the gutter and stuff his shirt with snow. Faces red as holly berries, mouths in a bubble of swearing, they dip and revel in the snow. The Market Clock strikes eight. Shaking the snow off their hair and coats, the girls skitter up the back stairs into the factory. The sparrows once more take possession of the street.

.   .   .

From John Dodder's room in Rotting Road the world looks like one huge snow-drift, heaving itself to the top of the Jubilee Hill. The air has that strange, after-snow mildness, as if it had precipitated all its cold as a brine solution precipitates its salt. Towards the south-east above the Rotting Road School, the grey of the sky is peeling off into hellebore-green.

He looks down at the allotments. It is as if the gardens from end to end were draped in muslin or thick spiders' web. You cannot see the shape of bush or frame but only mole-hills and bee-hives of snow. Only the stumps of brussels sprouts break through the undulations of the surface.

He leans over the window-sill and gazes along the street to the spot where, many operations ago, he used to play as a boy.   It was in the extreme corner of the gardens in a V-shaped nook with the high wall of St Kentigern's back street on the one side, and on the other the out-houses of the Conservative Club and the billboards that tell Waterloo Street what is good for it.   On the third side of the triangle, screening it from the allotments proper, had been a privet hedge with an old back-yard door let into it and a chain and padlock, to keep the boys off the pears and raspberries which old (then not old) Sprout grew for his shop.   But the pears had been past fruiting even when John Dodder was a lad, and the raspberries hid their few fruits in a thicket of bramble and wild grass.   He had known his way into that spot through a gap in the privet, and would sit, snug in the spring dusk, while the throstles shouted all round, and the cats stalked them among the struts of the hoardings.   There he could read penny thunders by the light of a flash-lamp or watch the couples through slits in the planks of the bill-boards, or even, through a knot-hole, dexterously spit on the trousers of the passers-by.

One year, when the snow was solid and lasting, they built a fort there—he and two others.   They shovelled the snow, shaping and slapping it like pounds of butter, and piled up the walls, and made an entrance tunnel under the privet.   In the after-tea dusk of Monday to Friday, and all day Sunday, they huddled together among their hoard of biscuit tins, old tyres, and packing straw. They drank lukewarm tea from ginger-beer bottles, and burnt brown paper in an old bucket.   They buried toffees in a tobacco tin and dug them up next day.   They believed the whole town would be looking for them and listened to the sound of it not finding them.   The dark froze down upon them, among the forests of the hoardings and the precipices of the closet walls, and they stayed, still and silent, till they whimpered with the cold.

' Oh, God!' says John Didder, slumping back on to his bed. ' I'll never spit at anybody again.   My spitting days are over.'

.   .   .

Now it is twelve o'clock and school is out and all those who do not stay behind for dinner are bounding down Trafalgar Street, the littles ones paddling up to the Wellington-tops in the drifts left on either side by the snow plough. Ten minutes to shovel in a plateful of hot stew or fish and chips, and then out again into the back streets and down to the Iron Green. The youngest of all have been there all the morning, waddling in snow up to their arm-pits. They are no longer playing with it or enjoying it, but try with a numb next-door-to-crying persistence, to scramble over the wall and climb the slag-bank. At every step they fall back, foxed and flummoxed by the snow, tripping over buried buckets, breaking their shins on hidden cobbles.

The elder boys are not deterred, however. They know their way about the slag-bank as a shepherd knows his way about the fells. They know every track and ledge in the slag; know how the rain has carved it into gulleys where now the snow lies deep as a crevasse; know how the surface of the slag is in parts rotten as scree, and in others hard as iron. They know, too, all the secret places of the bank : the nest of sandbags built during the War for the Home Guard; the ruins of Marsh Edge Farm that lies in an angle of the tip hidden from the town; the steps, cut in the slag-face, that lead down to the Ironworks Pier from which they can watch the boats. This slag-bank is very old—belonging, for the most part, to the last years of the last century, when smelting was so extravagant with ore that some people say there was more iron in the slag than in the pig. There has been no tipping here for many years, and already the bank seems to be slowly settling back into the earth from which it came. Today, it is settled entirely, and seems as ancient a part of the landscape as the sea or the fells. The snow drifts against its flanks, and collects in the creases and ghylls which split its sides, and piles up on ledges and parapets and corries. Every now and then clouds of steam from the cooling reservoirs of the furnaces float over the skyline. It is an Icelandic scene of snow and hot-springs, of glacier, rock, cliffs, sky, and sea-birds.

The boys are on top of the bank now, lolloping like arctic foxes from sleeper to sleeper of the old railway which brought the wagons to the tip. Here they are in their own kingdom, lifted high above the work-day world of fathers and policemen. Not one of these boys ever wants to go to the Pleasure Ground, with its swings and banana slide and such like juvenilia. Instead, they turn to this island plateau, with its cliff-coast and Table Mountain top, with its clefts and crannies, its almost-caves, its fastnesses and hide-outs. If they looked about them they would see one of the most magnificent views of England—the wedge of the estuary carved deeply out of the fells like a slice from a white-iced cake. But they are not concerned with views. They are concerned with the battle of boyhood, glad to ride the hours as a gull rides the wind. They know, also, that the slag-bank has a darker hour, when the dusk settles on it like a second, deeper, layer of snow, and the voices are not the voices of friends. Then, as they crouch behind the watchman's hut, they feel the brown darkness drumming with fear, as the whistles and boot-scratching draw nearer, until, in a last skitter of panic, they helter-skelter down the slag-side hardly noticing scrapes and bruises and tearing of trouser seats.

But now they have the bank to themselves and come glissading down a gulley in a skedaddle of snow. They are making for the pond or ' flash ' behind *The Furnace Arms*. It is a sump that gathers the seepage of the allotments where the water has lost its proper flow because of the pressure of the slag on the drains. The flash is frozen solid, not smooth and level, but crushed and hummocky, like arctic pack-ice. Already the lads have smashed the ice with iron bars and prized out great blocks of it, until now the pond, for the most part, lies dumped on dry land above its own shores. Old tins and rubber tyres which have lain at the bottom of the water for years are lifted high in the ice, displayed as in a glass case. The yellow reeds of last autumn poke their way through the snow, with a mound of driftage like a tiny rubble-tip against the side of each. Willows and poplars—boughs broken and bent and axed off till the trees take the shape of huge cacti—twist up from the frozen mud, their branches hanging with white lichen of snow. But there is nothing pathetic about them. Stubborn and persistent as a dialect, they go on year after year,

budding along their fractured and arthritic limbs. Many a
schoolboy generation has threatened amputation and massacre,
but the trees remain, chronically senescent yet obstinately alive.
Even now grey catkins are settling like snowflakes on the twigs of
the willow palm.

The sun comes out, and each boy is cartooned by his ironic
shadow, and the willows become black hands clutching up from
the snow. The snow-dazzle, here, has the brilliancy and wideness
of the Sahara sun, for this part of the town has nothing cramped
about it. When the people from Furnace Road visit the new
housing estates they feel hemmed in, for though they live in a
tight little terrace with back-yard behind, and rug-sized gardens in
front, they are used to a spaciousness that is due not to planning
but to the lack of plan. These small rows of houses look as if they
had been dumped down like baggage on a railway platform while
the owner goes for a sandwich. Those on Furnace Road face
across allotments and melancholy fields, that lead eventually to the
mines. The rest face nowhere. And about all of them is the
untidy spaciousness of land which has been forgotten, greens,
allotments, sumps, dumps, and slag-holes. *The Furnace Arms*
stands solid and square as a block of concrete, its door and eight
windows marking right-angles of shadow in the gleaming stucco.
It looks as isolated as an eighteenth century farmhouse among the
fells. Indeed, it is very like a farmhouse inside, with a flagstone
floor and a white deal table in the enormous, kitchen-like bar-
parlour, and clean sawdust every day in the Jubilee spittoons—

('A free pint if you cop the Queen in the eye,' says Chunker
Wilson.)

.   .   .

The boys return to school. The sun swings and sinks. Shadows
merge into the snow; the woodcut turns into a shadowy chalk
drawing. And the elder Miss Snoot at her window high up in
Old Odborough looks over the roofs of the town.

It is early evening. Snow and cloud are in collusion and the
town is more of a memory than a view. It is impossible to tell
which is earth and which is sky, though eastward what looks like

a whiter than usual cloud must surely be snow on the fells of
Furness.   Nearer, a blur of smoke and mist is simmering up from
the snow, among all the spikiness of spire and steeple, chimney-
stack and telegraph pole, the pinnacles of chapels and ventilators
of schools.   The houses of Old Odborough are already lighting
up for the evening, but it is not yet dark enough to see the lights
farther away.

Miss Snoot will be glad when it is dark.   She hates Odborough
and does not want to see more of it than need be.   When her
father retired she and her sisters begged him to take a bungalow
up the coast, but he insisted on remaining in Odborough, choosing
this house from where he can see, half a mile away, the roof and
chimney of the shop where he made his money.

He is sitting there now, fat and inanimate as a sack of flour,
staring out of the window as the lights come on.   Soon the blurred
sketch of the view will disappear and in its place will come an
entanglement of lights.   It is old Mr Snoot's ambition to learn to
recognise every one of them.   As the years go on he is gradually
charting his universe, plotting each constellation and learning the
names of every major star.   Straight ahead is what he calls Orion,
the three lights of the furnace top making the belt.   Away to the
south-west, well clear of the town, is the Plough or Great Bear—
six or seven distant lights scattered among the farms around
Oatrigg.   To the east, the lights of Beckside Station, across the
estuary, make the Little Bear.   And running diagonally across
his star-map is the Milky Way—the cream and dazzle of lights
that stretch from the goods-yard down the Ironworks sidings,
along the foot of the slag-bank, to the Ironworks themselves.

But it is no longer these stars of the first magnitude that hold
his fancy.   It is the lesser lights, the little twinkles from alley and
shop or upstairs window that no one but himself could attempt to
identify.   It fills him with strange satisfaction to think that while
the great illumination of the Market Square is quite invisible from
this point, the little lamps of Iron Green can be seen glowing
through a gap beyond Albert Road.   It is many years now since
he has visited the lower end of Odborough, for his legs will not
carry him up and down the hill, and he growls like a dog if any-

one suggests a car.   But the sight of a street-lamp or a window light that he can recognise hooks up memories like fish from a pool.   Then the night glows with an illuminated slide of *The Crown* Green, and the naphtha flares round the hobby horses, and Happy Homes Ltd., where he served his apprenticeship, bright as Jupiter in an extravagance of gas.

It is immensely difficult to identify these smaller lights.   He will fix his eyes on some spot that he thinks he knows and watch it intently as the day fades, hoping to be able to plot any light that may appear later on.   The view is always dimmed out, however, before the light declares itself, and there is a period of blurred dark when perspective shuts up like a concertina and the eye loses its bearings.   It would be easier, he thinks, at dawn, to fix his gaze steadily on one particular light and then to establish its place in the returning landscape.   But his daughters, on whom he is as dependent as a baby, refuse to get up in what they call the middle of the night to enable him to pursue his observations.

He glances towards Oatrigg, lifting his eyes to the other sky. Venus is powerful, in spite of the ground mist.   It strikes him suddenly that Venus is in the wrong place.   She does not belong in that unpeopled swash of sunset above the dunes and the sea. She belongs, surely, where he had seen her a thousand times as he came out of Happy Homes, just above the end pinnacle of the Wesleyan Methodist Chapel.   Perhaps on a hundredth of those thousand times, seeing her there, it had moved him to think how in so many towns like Odborough men were looking up at her as they shut shops or walked home from mills and mines.   And he would think how to each of them she had her proper place, to the left of the Town Clock or to the right of the water-tower—one single, certain planet shining across all the roofs of England.

He returns to his routine, but finds that once again he has failed.   While his thoughts were on Venus the landscape was rubbed away like chalk from a blackboard and he has lost the means of identifying the newly discovered stars.

His elder daughter crosses to the window.   There is an egali-tarianism about snow that she dislikes.   It is difficult to pretend not to see people when you are shuffling beside them in eighteen

inches of snow.   Her one thought now is : How long will it last?
She has malevolent memories of a fall—not so many years ago—
which had lasted from January to March.   It had not been a
very heavy fall to begin with—only about six to eight inches—
but when this was shovelled away another layer fell and then
another.   Or more truly, it did not seem to fall but to be precipitated out of the air.   Snowflakes drifted about permanently
as if they had come from nowhere, as if they had formed round
motes of dust like hoar-frost—which, in fact, is much the way in
which they *do* form.   The sky was grey, the air cold, dry, and
still.   Nothing seemed able to shift the snow.   It lay about like
huge drifts of gravel and dust.   It took the colour of dust—there
was not a sparkle or a gleam about it.   When you brushed it from
the path it lay unmelted in the little pile where you brushed it.
The Council men spaded it up from the streets and carted it in
lorries to Iron Green, and Odborough Old Quarry, where it
remained like a huge heap of rubble.   The children became bored
with it.   Birds and dogs were no longer puzzled by it—they had
forgotten that the world had ever been green.   Snow was not a
phenomenon that came and went.   It was something that was
always there.   Even the unburst snowballs lay at the side of the
road like cannon balls in the moat of one of Cromwell's ruins.

Miss Snoot moves as if to draw the curtains, but her father
forbids her with a shake of his head.   Not that he wants to look
out of the window any longer.   Instead, his mind is on the great
frosts of his youth, when the snow lay so deep on *The Crown*
Green that they had to dig a trench to the shop door.   When the
railway and the two roads were blocked with drifts, and not a
train or a letter or a newspaper came to the town for a week.
When old Aaron Tyson from Limestone Hill sold to the greengrocer's the turnips he'd stacked up for his sheep.   When women
went on their knees to Absalom Dale, of Cheap and Best, for a
handful of yeast.   When the Dunner froze at low tide and you
could skate from Odborough to Furness.   When it was so cold in
the winding shed at the mines that the men begged to go down the
pit to get warm.

He revels in the memory of it, making it froth and lather all round the alleys and back-yards of youth very nearly up to the roof-tops. It is a sign you are growing old when you do not enjoy the snow. But when you are indeed old, then you can enjoy it again. He does not have to worry any longer about the slither and the slush.

' Let it snow till it reaches the chimney-pots,' he says to himself.

Let it snow up to the Market Clock. Let the snow heap itself high as the slag-bank, high as the furnace chimneys, high as St Kentigern's steeple. In a warm blizzard of drowsiness he watches the snow sud and curdle over the roofs and spires of the New Town, mounting up the slope of Old Odborough, up the hill of the Main Street, till it reaches Mount Pleasant. And when at last it drifts through the window and fluffs all round his feet and legs, even then he does not let himself be disturbed.

.   .   .

Today, it is not so much a thaw as an apology. The snow has lost all its self-confidence. It shuffles back from the pavements; it yields the road to the traffic. It hems and haws off the roofs; it squirms away from the touch of water. John Dodder, from his window, sees the allotments a mottle of white and green like Gorgonzola cheese. Violet Moss, looking down Furnace Road on her way to the Grammar School, sees the slag-banks striped like a zebra. Miss Burns in Balmoral Road, at the foot of the hill of Old Odborough, finds a single crocus spiking through the snow, filing it as if it were an old letter. On the grass of the Jubilee Pleasure Ground the snow lies in a cold and embarrassed squiggle. Not even a dog wants to play with it now. The small children—of whom there are many about, for the junior schools are closed for the measles—kick their way contemptuously through it, refusing to recognise it as last week's friend. The cricket field wears a football jersey—parallel bars of ooze and snow marking the line of the drains. In gutters and spouts there is a drip and sniffle as if the houses had a bad cold in the head.

For this is churchyard weather. Nearly every morning the Catholic funerals process from St Joseph's to St Kentigern's, and nearly every afternoon the Protestants take their turn. The slow bell tolls more often than the Town Clock. It is as if the lives of the aged, preserved by the frost like fish in ice, rot away when the warmer air gets at them. This is the month when the Vicar meets parishioners whom he never sees for the rest of the year. He walks across the graveyard in his thick pneumonia jacket. Wreaths are piled high over Mr Snoot, died in his armchair counting stars.

('A just man,' said Canon Olds in the funeral oration.

'Nobbut just,' said Chunker Wilson.)

The melting snow dribbles off the sour daffodils—flowers forced in Cornish greenhouses to die resentfully on the graves of strangers. The bitter, unnatural yellow burns like acid into the dark ever-green of box and yew.

Under a sky as antiseptic as a scrubbed enamel bowl, 'flu colds, and measles brew and bubble. Old Odborough School, in the quarry-like playground dug out of the slope of the hill, is fretfully empty. Violet Moss, ordered back home after fainting in the gym, skids and stumbles through the dizzy Market Square, where her uncle is setting off to deliver the morning papers, four hours late. Old Mr Sprout is staying in bed—if anyone wants taties they can go and dig for them. Dr O'Brien moves along Albert Road like a canvasser, calling at every other house, letting himself in by the keys left in the doors. Old Postlethwaite stands outside the Cash Chemists, wrapped in layer after layer of cloth-ing like a water-pipe lagged against the frost, morosely counting prescriptions he won't have to dispense. Christopher Cracken-thwaite's top-hat becomes so familiar to the jackdaws at St Kentigern's that he's afraid they will start to build in it. The grave-digger complains that he is being worked to death.

.   .   .

Tonight, however, neither the 'flu nor the weather seem to matter. All over the New Town crowds are hurrying towards the Railway Bridge. Cars are coming in from the villages. There is a whirl of people in the open space between the Wreck and Old Odborough School. For this is Opera Week. A month ago the professional producer, or 'coach', arrived from London and took lodgings with Contralto Ethel. Since then the company has rehearsed every night of the week and on Saturday afternoons —a proposal to rehearse on Sundays having been defeated by the threatened resignation of more than half the Vice-Presidents. For four weeks they have coughed and catarrhed their way through a fever of practising. 'Flu descended on them like a thunderstorm and left them doddering but determined. One after the other the chorus girls collapsed at rehearsal, stayed away for two nights, and then returned. Jack Edwards lost his voice and whispered through the part so that rehearsals should not be interrupted. The 'character' soprano had a week in bed with pleurisy, and then appeared on the second night and insisted on taking over from the understudy, who has since resigned, together with her husband, the principal flute. Snow on the railway delayed some of the hired costumes so that Her Majesty's Royal Guards were commanded by a Captain of the Fire Brigade, that being the only similar uniform which could be borrowed at short notice. The Chairman made dozens of telephone calls trying to locate the scenery, which had been shunted into a siding in a remote Pennine junction—now snowed-up—and had to be brought to Odborough by road in one of Crackenthwaite's lorries. Of the two little boys who were to have appeared as royal pages, one has caught measles and the mother of the other caught a scare, so their blouses have been let out and the parts played by two girls from the chorus. One of the dancers developed a twinge in the spine and squealed with pain whenever she had to bend, but refused to retire. A hysteria of sore throats and shivers made the entire cast dizzy with apprehension. They went on the stage smelling of cough lozenges, lung tonic, embrocation, and camphorated oil.

But the first night came, the show went on, and tonight is the third night.

The Recreation Hall was built at the beginning of the century by a company of local share-holders, most of whom had sub-scribed no more than £10. It is a rectangular building, bare as a factory, with a basement for billiards, and with lawns at the side

intended for bowls and tennis. The company was formed with
the support of The Young Men's Self-Improvement Club, and
aimed at providing means for healthy exercise and beneficial
entertainment in an atmosphere of temperance, mutual service,
and goodwill. But in 1918 the building had been sold to a
cinema firm, and now it is only in Opera Week that it reverts to
its true function.

There is perhaps no other event of the town year which attracts
so large a proportion of the townsfolk. No class or category is
excluded. The very poorest—even in the time of the slump—
would queue on the first night for a shilling seat in the Fish Market
under the balcony. Workers, shopkeepers, clergy, teachers,
farmers—all go to the Opera. Even the Managing Director of
the Ironworks, who will condescend to attend no other local
function, takes his place in the front row of the Balcony on the
Nob's Night.

He is sitting there now, with half a dozen officials of the society,
most of them in evening-dress, hurrying to speak to him. There
seem to be more officials showing people to their seats than there
are people to be shown, though the hall is filling fast. Everyone
in the society who does not appear on the stage seems to be
selling programmes. The audience is so excited that it is a
wonder that the hall does not blow up. All the better seats have
been booked for three weeks. About eight to ten people
queued all night in the snow to obtain tickets for the Saturday
performance. Tonight, too, a bus-load of visitors has arrived
from the society at Furness, and they wait, eager as women at a
rummage sale, to snatch and criticise.

The crowd buzzes like a dynamo. Everyone is turning, waving
to friends, stuffing coats under the seat, opening boxes of choco-
lates, scratching for change, blowing noses. Small boys in the
front now lean over the balcony rail and are grabbed by the pants
and hauled back. Mrs Makeweight, discovered to be occupying
somebody else's seat, refuses to move until the Secretary, the
Treasurer, the Chairman, and the Inspector of Police are able to
persuade her that the mistake was hers and not that of Mrs Moss,
the newsagent's wife, who was responsible for the booking. Old

Mr Sprout, his long neck swathed in scarf upon scarf like a leek, glances round to see where the draught is coming from. The orchestra begins to assemble. The red velvet curtain at its central parting is constantly tweaked open, as the girls of the chorus peep to see if their families have arrived; catastrophic crashes are heard behind the stage, as if the whole scenery had collapsed. Christopher Crackenthwaite enters from the door beside the stage and walks down the steps to the conductor's stand. Some of the lights are switched off, but the talk, as yet, scarcely diminishes. The conductor begins the overture, and for a time one listens in astonishment to a sound which seems unlike anything that could be produced by human means. It is a strange eerie wailing— the voice, maybe, of unknown creatures on a ghostly planet. Slowly the ear gropes for the note like a hand groping for a stone in muddy water. The piano asserts itself. The professional violinist who is leading the orchestra takes a determined grasp on the melody. Soon the voices will join in, the woodwinds will blow themselves into tune, and the ear will recover from its surprise. The overture ends, and the applause which follows is a signal for silence rather than a sign of appreciation. The rest of the lights are lowered and the curtain rises.

The Amateur Operatic Movement emerged from two conflicting tendencies : on the one hand, love of the theatre; on the other, disapproval. Nineteenth-century Nonconformity (a most powerful force in the shaping of Odborough) was resolutely opposed to the stage, but the people who belonged to Nonconformity were not. They practised what was still a dramatic religion. They knew how to sing, and had been brought up in the essentially operatic tradition of Handel. Feeling themselves caught between their inclinations and their principles, they approached the stage cautiously, beginning with oratorios, and going on to Gilbert and Sullivan and, later, to the Edwardian operettas, and in this way they were able to endow the theatre with the respectability of the choral union.

Now this dual ancestry—religious and secular, Puritan and Cavalier—gave to the movement an extraordinarily firm place in the society of its time. It drew its members from almost every

class and division.   It was able to ignore political and denominational differences.   The chapel choirs joined because it gave them
another chance to sing.   The viola joined—ignoring the tawdri-
ness of the music—because it gave him a chance to play.   The
actor joined—ignoring the triviality of the libretto—because it
gave him the chance to act.   The girls joined because it allowed
them to assume an elegance inappropriate to Trafalgar Road, and
even in a subdued, long-skirted manner, to show they could dance.
For them, as indeed for the whole town, the event became a
co-operative day-dream, a gilded and garlanded emanation of the
longings and fantasies and self-deceptions of a whole community.
It is not insignificant that the society was known, simply and
almost ostentatiously, as The Amateurs.   No one thought of
asking : Amateurs of what?

.   .   .

Between the ages of six and sixteen I missed none of the annual
productions of the Odborough Society.   I was taken first of all
by my father, who on that one Saturday afternoon of the year,
would shut up shop and go over to the hall to show the matinée
patrons to their seats.   Then, after having told some other responsible person to keep an eye on me, he left me—small, silent, and
completely enchanted.   Of the first production, in 1920, all that
remains in the memory is a coffin, or maybe a stretcher, carried
across the stage.   But from this time onwards I attended with
growing comprehension and never lessening wonder.

It was the time of the Edwardian operettas.   An age which
had been shelled out of existence by the War still lingered on
among the amateur societies like comfrey and feverfew in the
garden of a demolished cottage.   Pretty little buds of melody
flowered among the waste of the slump and the jazz.   I remember
the shoe-buckles of *Tom Jones,* with a golden retriever on the
stage, petted by the chorus; the policeman of *A Princess of
Kensington* who fainted flat twice in every performance; the
barge that floated across the back-cloth in *Miss Hook of Holland*;
Cingalee, with the stage darkened, and a brown-stained chorus
singing to a spotlight of a moon; *San Toy,* with its knowing

chinkery-tinkery, its jangle and tinsel; *The Duchess of Dantzig* and *Nell Gwynne,* with characters I knew about, Napoleon and Charles II, looking as I knew they looked and speaking as the ironmonger and the milkman spoke. I remember the fifteen-stone tenor as Oberon, King of the Fairies, singing:

' I do ride upon a swallow——— '

(' Oh, my God, you must be hollow,' said Chunker Wilson in the Fish Market.) I remember the beloved buffooneries of the comedian, a barber who sang like Figaro; the soubrette, who could convey in a wink a whole lost age of back-stair humour; the singing heroes whose names remain among our local worthies, legendary as John Peel, long after their voices had cracked and their subscriptions expired.

But more than all these, more than the clowning, the grotes-queries, the melodrama, I see a strange, green incandescence, painted canvas leafing and branching, a blossoming of calico and limelight. The willow pattern of China, the moonbeams of Ceylon, fade from my mind. It is a nearer-to-hand scene which remains—the glades of *Merrie England* and a *Country Girl*; oaks dropping chorus girls like acorns; lawns and rides and clearings opening into dream beyond dream of green perspectives; shadowed side-screens, thick as bracken, folded and doubled one over the other. I see ribbons and smocks and garters; ale-mugs topped with froth as Scafell Pike is topped with cloud; girls whose bare arms were a flutter of sunlight in a birch-wood. In the half-dark, when the footlights went down at Trysting Time, the branches were thridded with owls and squirrels and the roots smouldered with glow-worms. And all of it was lifted in a huge green wave of song—men and women singing like a gale in the forest, roaring until the boughs rocked and fern and frond blew straight into the eyes and ears of the watchers to settle in the leaf-mould of memory.

These annual events, in fact, took on a significance far beyond their artistic merit. In spite, often, of fluffed lines, delayed entries, stumbling dances, shoddy scenery, behind-stage jealousies, there was created an imaginative whole, a transfiguration of the

E

crudest common denominator of desires. Shop-girls and typists,
all of them known to everyone by their Christian names, flicking
their flounces, flashing their bare legs, gathered about themselves
something of the mystery of Botticelli graces. The show had
become a ritual.

As the twenties moved on, the Edwardian confidence faded.
The Young Men's Self-Improvement Club was forgotten.   The
choral work became less conscientiously four-part.   On Saturday
night the comedian permitted himself the occasional swear-word.
With the thirties came tap-dancing, bare midriffs, trick-lighting,
and half-jazz.   The old operettas were still presented from time
to time, but the charm, the prettiness, the Edwardian archness had
disappeared.   Today it is the grandiose vulgarity of the American
musicals that most of the societies try to imitate.

Yet the spirit of the movement has changed very little.   Go
behind the stage at Odborough, and you will find the same
excitement, the same commotion, whether the show is *Floradora*
or *The Desert Song, The Pirates of Penzance* or *Oklahoma*.

It is Saturday night, now, and the back-stage is crowded.
Below, in the basement, a row of helpers is making tea and washing up at a trestle table.   Committee men, programme sellers,
mothers of the chorus, visitors from other societies, stand about
chatting as at a party.   The entire company is on the stage at the
moment.   There is a distant murmur of the orchestra, the thump
of the dancers.   A cymbal clangs, followed by the sound of
applause.   One is reminded, almost with surprise, that an
audience is present, for here that audience is quite forgotten.   The
chorus clatter down the two winding staircases which lead from
either side of the stage, girls unbuttoning their dresses and half
wriggling out of them, making ready for their quick reappearance
in the finale of the first act.   They accept a cup of tea as they
pass, and scrimmage through the crowd to the curtained recess
where they change.

With the chorus out of the way for a minute or two there is
room, upstairs, behind the wings.   Ardent arguments are taking
place in groups of two or three.   There is so much noise that it
seems impossible for the audience to hear what is being said on

the stage. Every now and then the prompter hisses for silence. Beside her the principal scene-shifter sits on a crate of bottles, a dancing girl on each of his knees and his hands on the curtain rope. Jack Edwards stands deliberately apart, concentrating on his lines. The leading lady, in a polka of debate, is suddenly seized by the producer and pushed through the wings into the stage, where, like a duck thrown into the pond, she instantly takes to the water and begins to swim.

The beer is going round. Some of the chorus are being kissed in corners and some not in corners at all. Larking has begun. On the stage the consequential innkeeper presents to Milord on a salver a card on which is inscribed a single rude word. Milord hides a smile with a flick of his glove, folds the card, and hands it casually to the second soprano.

'Where's Bobby?' says the producer. 'He's due on in half a minute.'

The call goes down the stairs, through the basement, into the dressing-rooms, into the Gents' and, failing that, the Ladies'. The leading lady and the innkeeper desperately improvise a misunderstanding over chairs, which—as much to their embarrassment as to their relief—turns out to be funnier than what they ought to be doing. Bobby is discovered outside, leaning over the fence of the cricket field in the pitch dark, contemplating Jupiter. He is thrust upstairs and on to the stage, trips over his spurs, and falls with the grace of what seems to be perfect rehearsal into the arms of the leading lady. He twines his hands round her neck and hangs in a dead weight, panting to get his breath back.

'Which bloody act are we supposed to be doing?' he whispers, as the audience rumble with delight.

But, behind stage, the crisis has hardly been noticed. The show goes on like a machine, like a giant-stride in a children's playground, on which every member of the company jumps now and then for a ride, and then jumps off and lets the whole contraption keep turning without him. The chorus are back upstairs now, herded like sheep at a gate, waiting for the final entry of the first act. There is a conspiratorial glee among them, for someone has substituted a bottle of port wine for the bottle of cold tea from which the innkeeper will have to fill their glasses. The leader of the chorus, who is standing in the wings in view of the audience, is aware behind her of that which, being in view of the audience, she is unable to prevent. Whatever may be the show on the stage, behind scenes is always *Merrie England*.

.   .   .

This is the true significance of the amateur operatic movement. It is the descendant, in an urban society, of the primitive fertility cults. For the myth of the dying and reviving god, of the sacred marriage between sun and soil, the magical cults to bring rain and crops, all survived, until very recently, in the seasonal festivals and superstitions of country folk—May Queens, Rose Queens, Morris Dancers, Midsummer Fires, Hallowe'en, mistletoe, rice at weddings, April Noddies and May Goslings. All this is well known in the post-Frazer world. But it is not so often realised that when these customs died out with the coming of the industrial era man did not suddenly become independent of the seasons. His fundamental needs remain what they always were. He depends, as he always did, on the sun, on the forces of air and water, on the fertility of the soil, on the yearly renewal of the green world. For many men, indeed, this fact is obscured by the mechanisation of society. They forget it with their minds; but in their hearts they still know it is true. The seasonal festivals may have become cheapened and commercialised, the Easter daisies drenched with petrol instead of dew and Simnel Sunday rented out to sweet and flower shops—but they still help to satisfy a fundamental human desire. For today, as much as ever, man needs to adjust himself to the seasonal rhythm of nature, to the growth of grass and tree, to the alternation of sun and wind and rain. He finds it impossible, however, to revive the old customs. Much as they may appeal to the deeper levels of the imagination, they seem to his conscious mind to be archaic, irrelevant, and even silly. But in the amateur operatic movement he can indulge in myth-making without knowing what he is doing. He can't be primitive and almost up to date at one and the same time.

The resemblance between the operettas and May Day and the

festivals is quite remarkable. First of all there is the central figure of the spring goddess or leading lady, chosen like the May Queen, from among the local girls, courted and complimented by the whole society, saluted with flowers and ceremoniously kissed by the Chairman on the last night. Then there are her attendants, the chorus girls and the dancers, with their ribbons and posies; her clown, the comedian; her guard, a retinue of soldiers—the ' Green Men ' of the woods. Often there is a dog on the stage or a pony or a parrot, representatives of the natural order of beast and bird. Then, again, there is all the elaborate make-up and masking, the dressing up and undressing, bare shoulders among the leafy boughs; there is the scenery of palace and woodlands, like the ' Green Booths ' of the Festival of Tabernacles; and frequently there is female impersonation or a girl dressed as a boy, the confusion and interchange of the sexes—all familiar features of the old May Day festivals.

The final call has now been taken. The entire company is on the stage for the Queen. Tommy Dale wraps yet another scarf round his head, and with uplifted voice begins to praise, not the production he has just seen, but that of *The Mikado*, which he had seen (and unlike the present one, had also heard) in 1910, when the society was first founded. On the stage, the presentations begin. To the producer, to the conductor, to the prompter, and the stage manager. The principals present one another with bunches of flowers—like Russian footballers. The cheering renews itself in multiples of three. The men being to gyrate, as in the lancers, kissing each girl as they pass. The mother of the leading lady comes round with a couple of clothes baskets to carry home the presents. Jack Edwards and some of the older men have packed their cases and are ready to depart, feeling the weight of ten or twenty shows descending on them like autumn leaves. But the young girls are as wide awake as if the show were only beginning on the first night. They have not changed from their costumes of the last act, and some of them are going off to farewell parties in shops and parlours which will last until two or three in the morning. The next day they will cry with tiredness, the make-up not yet properly wiped off their eyes, and all the trouble of packing and returning the costumes and scenery yet to be done. Sunday after Opera is a blank and bleak day. But their duty has been carried out. The ritual has been performed. The return of spring has been made certain, the crops have been secured. Fertility has been promoted, and will come to some of them, perhaps, sooner than they had reckoned on.

March

OLD MR SPROUT locks the door of his shop, steps into the street, stands for a moment wheezing like an harmonium, and then pops a chlorodyne sweet into his mouth.   These March evenings are treacherous.   The days lengthen out a bit and you deceive yourself into thinking winter is over, but more often than not winter is yet to come.   The great star is shining out of a glowing sky, and the throstles, in allotments and back-gardens, are probing the dusk with lancets of sound.

Mr Sprout turns towards the station end of Rotting Road, rheuming and spluttering into the cold dregs of the light, regretting the warm dark of mid-winter.   Suddenly he coughs to a standstill as a body skims round the corner, brakes, skids, and windmills six inches from the old man's waistcoat.

' Roller skates !' says Mr Sprout.

He pushes out a hand that sends the boy spinning across the road like a drunken tight-rope walker and then pauses and listens

to the creak of other skaters, unseen, round the corner.   There is
a stampede of footsteps.   Boys' voices clatter.

'Glory,' says Mr Sprout.   'The streets are full of children.
They've hatched out like greenfly in the afternoon sun.'

And, indeed, he is right.   For while Mr Sprout and a thousand
others are deploring the catarrhal longevity of winter, the children
have already accepted the spring.   Now, in the after-tea half-
light, they swarm among all the streets of the town.

It is a brutal time of day and time of year.   No use for football
or rounders or any game that you can umpire.   Instead, the
town child reverts to a society as primitive as palaeolithic man.
There are hidings away, searchings, chasings, scroungings, and
scuffles.   There are the first encounters of sex against sex.   There
are moments of complete and terrifying loneliness.

Young Tyson, Mr Sprout's grandson, is standing in the Albert
Entry, spying out the land.   The Entry is the assembly ground,
the rally green, of all the children in this part of the town.   It is,
in fact, merely a gap between two blocks of terrace houses, giving
access from Albert Road into the back street.   On either side
of it rises a great slate house-end, unbroken except for a small attic
window in the peak of the roof.   Opposite is the back street of
Gladstone Terrace and the unbuilt-on land between there and
Rotting Road, so that the Entry is open to the afternoon sun and
becomes hot as an oven in summer.   Here, out of reach of the
traffic, are played all the games that require space and freedom
from interruption—cricket, with wickets chalked on the walls,
football with the Entry ends for the goals, Tin Can Norkey,
Cannon Sticks, Stick o' Roger, Leap-Frog, Horehound, and
Spanish Fly.   And here, because of its strategic position at the
confluence of so many front or back streets, is the place for Tally
Hoo Dogs and all the other peripatetic games.

Young Tyson slips out of the Entry, crosses the Albert Road,
and runs in the direction of Back Rotting Road.   He does not
really belong here.   His father keeps the tripe and poultry shop
in Trafalgar Road, but by right of frequent visits to his grandfather's he has come to know the Rotting Road group and been
allowed to join it.   It is a quiet, unmalicious group of boys and

girls from seven to about twelve, and Timothy Tyson—who is by nature as timid as a chaffinch—feels less scared of them than of the Slag-bank Rovers of his own doorstep. Moreover, the presence of the girls means that the games tend towards fantasy rather than banditry.

They are playing, now, a hide-and-seek of which the frontiers are defined as clearly as a robin's territory: Albert Road and Victoria Street from the railway down to *The Crown* Green and the Wesleyan Chapel, and all streets from there up to Rotting Road, the Co-op, and Waterloo Road. Young Tyson moves into the hinterland behind his grandfather's shop which is that part of earth he knows best. The topography here is more complex than it appears to the passer-by in the front streets. Albert Road and Victoria Street belong to the late-nineteenth-century development of Odborough—two of four parallel streets, laid down in a grid, where all is straight and ruled and not a square yard is unaccounted for. But round the edges of the grid the geometrical order does not hold. Between Albert Road and Rotting Road—streets as respectable as the Band of Hope—there is a gap in the jigsaw, a triangle fitted into the rectangle, where is now a wynd and ghetto of sheds, small warehouses, stables turned into garages, a forge, a Council dump, and bits of gardens fenced off by tarred corrugated iron. Young Tyson moves along the hypotenuse, with Back Gladstone Terrace on his left, till he reaches the place where the sheds fall away from a hen-scratch of ground planted with poles for washing-lines—like stakes driven into a shallow shore in wartime to impede landing-craft. He stands here in a three-cornered cloister of stillness. Around him, against the egg-blue sky, the roofs spike up, gothic as Notre Dame—the spire of the Liberal Club, the turret of the Co-operative Hall, the stove-pipe of his grandfather's banana house. Among the sheds, from an apple-tree as black as iron, a thrush is shouting.

Young Tyson lurks in the shadow of the warehouse, peeping round the corner to see if anyone is following. But no one is. They rarely follow him, for he chooses just this one place, with his grandfather's back door close to hand, and the shops of Rotting Road round the corner. The others choose the adventurous

streets on the farther side of Albert Road, where there are more
alleys and more hazards—strangers, dogs, policemen, foraging
bands of boys from the slag-bank.   There, among the tell-tale
lights, there are distant spyings, recognitions, shouted challenges,
and long races to the home base.   Timothy Tyson keeps clear of
all that.   In his cathedral close of quiet he plays at hide with only
the throstles to seek.   The dusk thickens around the chimney-
pots and floats downward.   Lights come on in some of the back-
room bathrooms, throwing little search-beams along the closet
roofs.   He crouches in the shadows, skulks in a garage doorway,
cringes into the shelter of a gate-post, hiding like a hunted Indian.
And there is no one to hide from.   He waits longing to be sought
for, or, at least, to hear the All-in-all-in-all-in-all-in which will
recall him to base.   But no one comes and no one calls.   The
silence presses on him.   The roofs are goblined with smoke.   Fear
tightens on his fingers like frost.   He hears a footstep that is not
that of a boy approach from the railway end of the back street,
and with a gulp of thankfulness and disappointment recognises his
grandfather.

Old Sprout tries the lock of the banana-house, gently Cwm-
Rhondda-ing under his breath.   It might seem easier to come
through the house and back-yard instead of walking round the
block, but years ago, in his first lock-up business on *The Crown*
Green, he had learned to shut-up-shop by shutting himself out,
and the habit cannot now be broken.   He catches a glimpse of
Timothy skedaddling down the back street but gives no sign.
His daughter, who has ideas above her tripe shop, objects to the boy
playing in the back streets, but the old man can see no harm in it.
Sixty years ago the back street had been for him his clubroom,
his gymnasium, his catacomb, and his trysting place.   There is
not an entry, an alley, a gateway, a wall, a yard, a shed, or a hen-
house, that he doesn't know as well as any lad on the rampage
tonight.   He enters Albert Road, where the street-lamps, just
switched on, twinkle all the way through boyhood back into the
beginnings of the town.   Here at the top end, he is among streets
he has seen grow out of the bare ground.   These are the houses of
the prosperous nineties, the houses of the Boer War: Victoria

Street faced with yellow freestone (though underneath it was
Cumberland slate, like all the rest) and called the Khaki Road at
the time of enlistment. The town had sneaked away from it,
leaving it marching from nowhere to nowhere, yet it had not lost
its look of confidence. It belonged to an Empire that was sure of
itself and a Queen who would live for ever. The houses of the
new Council estates would fall in and be slums again long before
the slates came off the roofs of Victoria Street.

To Mr Sprout, however, it still seems an interloper, a raw
intrusion. He hears the thrushes singing as they used to do from
old Absalom Dale's orchard, and looking northward, across the
railway, he sees the sky green as a lettuce over Old Odborough.
And once again he sees the Rotting Pool land as, for him, it has
always been : the flat, reedy pasture lying beside the marsh, field
drains oozing slowly towards the Pool. He is walking now, in the
middle of Victoria Street, along this very lane, up to the shins in
mud, as he had walked every morning to Old Odborough School.
He is crossing the very bridge with two low walls and a splash for
cattle, where the lane crossed Rutty Beck. He knows every
meandering of this beck, from where it rose on the Jubilee Hill,
crossed the Market Square, down St Kentigern's Terrace, and
under Rotting Road just where the ironmonger's was, three shops
away from his own. All this was underground, of course, blocked
and bricked over in his father's time, but the rest he remembers
well enough. It came out of its culvert below the Liberal Club,
flowed under the lane at right angles, curved east nearly as far as
the Green, then doubled back on itself and wriggled under the
Ironworks Railway to join Rotting Pool just above high marsh
level. He can draw the course of it as on a map—under Moss's
Newsagents, St Kent's Temperance Hotel, Smith's Ironmongers,
Back Gladstone Terrace, Mrs Dawson's Hot Pies, Teddy Lew-
thwaite's on one side of Victoria Street and the little insurance
agent's on the other, the caretaker's of St Joseph's and Chunker
Wilson's sister that married the Pole in Kimberley Terrace. And
every blessed house was damp. The water still keeps to its old
course, under pavement and terrace exhaling a mildewed breath.

' Glory !' says Mr Sprout. ' Shall we gather at the river !'

He walks now in a miasma of memory. The electric lamps hang along the line of willows that divided field from field. Children infest the landscape, shouting, running, climbing the hedges, jumping over the becks. He sucks another chlorodyne against the damps and walks on oblivious.

Yet others are not oblivious of him. As he moves down the road towards the Green two figures can be seen darting along from cover to cover. They are Chunker Wilson's two nephews, tracking. When the old man turns the corner they race through the gap behind the lodging-house and watch him pass the end of the back street. He is walking slowly now, peering short-sightedly into the twilight. They hurry after him, and overtake, miming unconcern. This is the moment for real finesse. They cross Albert Road, slip into the back street, over the wall of the Wesleyan Schoolroom by a route they know as well as their own bedroom stairs, across the school yard at full rip, round behind the Chapel, into the outside Gents', over the wall into the plasterer's yard, through a broken slat in the fencing into Back Waterloo Road, and in five seconds they are nonchalantly kicking a lamp-post as Mr Sprout passes the front door of the Chapel. He stares, puzzled, and passes by. They grab hands and maypole with delight round the lamp-post. Such moments are the reward of their skill. It is easy to track people in summer when the streets are crowded and no one takes any notice of a small boy. It is possible, then, to follow a woman through her whole week-end's shopping or even to track a courting couple on a Saturday evening. But at this time of year, with few people about, it takes real enterprise, real ingenuity.

Mr Sprout, making for Waterloo Road, hesitates, stops, and turns round. For a moment the boys think he is going to face and challenge them—the most humiliating defeat that can come upon any tracker. Instead, he turns into the back street. They look at one another, surprised. Here is something that challenges not only their honour as trackers, but also their curiosity. They peep after him. He is going along steadily, not hurrying, not looking back. Apart from him, the street is empty. This is the time when black shadows come out for the night, like cats, though above the chimney-pots, telegraph wires, and television aspirates still gleam in the sunset. Mr Sprout suddenly turns a corner and disappears. The boys can scarcely believe what they see. They chase along to the corner and reconnoitre. He is going down a practically never-used little back street leading to Albert Road. They follow, keeping always one corner of the block behind him. He doubles back like a fox. Round Mrs Dawson's corner, up Gladstone Terrace behind the Co-op, across to Back Rotting Road, down to the Liberal Club. The lads have never been so excited in their lives. Children appear and disappear in twos and threes from alley and entry and road end, hiding, seeking, hopping, scotching—but the two take no notice. Timothy Tyson glances timidly at his grandfather and sneaks away. Above the roofs the Market Clock begins to glow a pale primrose against the dimming sky.

The old man walks slowly past the back of his own warehouse and round into Back Rotting Road, pausing for a while at the corner and looking about him. The boys freeze into the shadow, and then advance, cautiously, keeping close to the fences and garages. They hesitate. Old Mr Sprout can be heard rheuming away, out of sight, and the smell of chlorodyne tinges the dark. The elder boy moves on. Suddenly his arms are gripped above the elbows from behind and he is jerked into a dark gap between the tarred wood of the warehouse and the corrugated door of the garden fence.

' Following me ?' asks the old man.

' Oh, no, Mr Sprout.'

' Yes, you were. And making nobbut a poor job of it. I spotted you outside the Chapel.'

He relaxes his grip, but the boy, though still puzzled, does not run away.

' Come along here,' says the old man. ' And I'll show you.'

He steps back into the gap between wall and fence to where it seems blocked by a large sheet of corrugated iron. Taking this in his hands, he bends it forward, so that a crack appears between iron and wood, through which he steps into a little corridor that leads into Back Rotting Road.

'There you are,' says Mr Sprout. 'That fence has been loose for half a century. Many a time, as a lad, I've diddled people by slipping round the corner and through here so that I was behind them when they thought I was in front.'

He stands stock-still in a halo of chlorodyne while the throstles of sixty years whistle through his ears.

'Following me,' he says. 'I'll tell you one thing, me lads. It won't be so long before you'll be following me somewhere else.'

The boys stare at him, uncomprehending but asking no questions.

He raises a hand and points to the sky.

'I'll be waiting for you up yonder,' he says. 'When the time comes I'll be saying to Mr Wilson: Now where's those two nephews of yours?'

The boys, brought up in their father's religion, think this extremely unlikely, but say nothing.

'And now,' says Mr Sprout, 'If you'll fetch my grandson, who ought to be laiking about somewhere, I'll see if I can find you a jaffa apiece.'

.   .   .

This morning from my attic window I can hear the wind roaring in the street, brushing and scrubbing the flagstones and turning its reversed vacuum cleaner on the slates and shop-fronts. Around the Co-op Corner it whines like a saxophone, and in Waterloo Street it twangs and creaks, swinging the sign of the Cash Chemists and plucking at the sun-blinds. Smoke from the railway is ballooned out and goes sailing over the roofs, white as a starched shirt in the early sun.

This is the time when the boys begin to trot over the Railway Bridge to Old Odborough School—Timothy Tyson having to trail all the way from Trafalgar Road because his mother thinks Old Odborough is more refined than Rotting Road. He has no bell to encourage him now as I had when I used to cross that bridge to the same school. In those days Old Odborough still had the character of a village and the boys were country boys, even though the fathers of most of them worked, if they worked at all, at the mines or the Ironworks. They knew every hole in a wall, every gap in a hedge, for miles around. They could hunt across meadow and ploughland right under the eyes of the farmer and never be seen. They ratted and bird-nested, caught tiddlers and paddocks, stoned the spadgers and set dogs on the rabbits. They ripped armfuls of bluebells out of the woods in spring, and gathered basket-loads of blackberries in autumn, selling them at the doors for a penny a pound.

For Old Odborough is at the waist, where the country pinches in on either side, and the town is no more than one road wide. The school is just beyond the bridge at the foot of the hill of Old Odborough. Here, at the point where the rock begins to show its teeth, a quarry-like hollow has been dug out. On the one side, the road and the houses and the hill curve above it like a turned-up collar. But on the other, the playground slopes into the cricket field with, beyond it, the meadows and farmland running out towards the sea.

The school itself seems part of the hill, being built of that very slate which has been blasted away to make room for it. Looked at from the road, it is a dibble of steep roofs, gable ends, peaked windows, porches, chimneys, ventilators, and turrets, over which, nevertheless, it is still possible to get a good view of a cricket match without having to pay. The playground which once belonged to the Infants is barricaded by an outcrop of bare rock down which, already, the ivy-leaved toadflax is dribbling a few mauve flowers. The boys' playground, on the other hand, looks into the turf of the field, the first leaf of elder, and the huge hullabaloo of the sky.

But when you enrolled at the Boys' Department, after leaving the Infants, you saw none of this. For the school had been built round a yard or quadrangle. Maybe the intention had been to leave this open to the sky, but in my time it was roofed in with opaque glass, so that to step inside was like stepping into one of those translucent mists of spring. You were doused in light, yet you could see nothing. All around you were whitewashed walls and above you was a perpetually cloudy sky. It was a room where there were no shadows. The space behind the blackboard was as bright as that in front. Ink-wells, rulers, copy-books, the stove, the stove-pipe, the fire-guard, stood preserved as in a jelly of light. It had its own quietness. The sound of the world outside never reached it through the surrounding rooms. The sound of other classes and other teachers seemed irrelevant to little boys who did not yet feel part of the community of the school. Hail drummed on the roof, and when it rained cans and jam-jars were disposed to catch the drips, and the desks were arranged round the pools and splashes like streets round the canals and lagoons of Venice. The room was completely without ventilation, and in winter became a refrigerator of dead-still draughtless cold. We could see our breath rising in the air like floating hoar-frost. In summer the dead air expanded as in a greenhouse, and pressed clumsily on our temples. We drowsed and snorted, half-choked by the smell of hot socks, sweat, unwashed hair, ink, chalk, and stale disinfectant. The whitewash restricted our gaze on every side, and only when a gull let on the roof and left a slightly whiter patch behind it on the white glass did we have any news of the world outside.

The old man who taught us—and who had taught my father forty-one years before—would retire behind the blackboard every now and then to chew tobacco. He taught—as, indeed, we learned—by habit. Regular as the tides, twice a day, the same words came pounding against our undefended shores, and slowly they wore away resistance, making deep grooves in our memory. Nothing that I learned in that first year, aged seven or eight, has ever been forgotten.

My companions were boys of an iron time in an iron town. Born into war rations and bred on the dole, they lived in a world where poverty seemed too natural to complain about. Those from the workless homes dangled feet in huge clumsy clogs provided by the local police from their annual Footwear Ball. Their heads jerked out of the collarless necks of their shirts like a sweep's brush out of chimney-pot. The others showed varying degrees of shabby elegance and mother's pride—celluloid Eton collars with bow-ties, woollen jerseys buttoned up to the neck, and, in my own

case, a sailor suit. These were the sons of clerks and shopke
who would slip through the Secondary School as through a
door and escape from the town. The rest would stay. Some of
them I see nearly every day—friends and acquaintances whose
lives have run parallel for forty years, never meeting and yet
getting no farther apart. Others have been quite lost sight of.
But sometimes, in the street or at a cricket match, a face will
appear which I can give no name to, can relate to no circumstance
or person, and which is yet tantalisingly familiar. The brand of
the old quadrangle does not easily wear off.

The quadrangle itself, however, no longer exists. Its floor is
asphalted and open to the sky and forms a space between the two
separate blocks of the now reconstituted school. Today it is
empty. The boys, having arrived at nine o'clock, found the
school closed for measles. Timothy Tyson returns home for his
whip and top and then begins to spin his ambitions up and down
Trafalgar Back Street, knowing that he need fear no alarms until
dinner-hour, as the Rotting Road Schools have not been closed.
He whips steadily and earnestly, crouching over the top, not even
straightening his back when he runs. The top, thin and tall as a
clothes-peg, leaps high in the air at the feel of the lash, skipping
twenty yards. He darts after it among the clothes-props and the
washing, for it is Monday; and among the milk-carts and coal-
lorries and old prams loaded with sacks of coke. He dodges round
women pegging out shirts that twist like wrestlers in the bullying
wind. They take no notice whatever, being used to these Lenten
humours, for now is the time that the Passion symbols take the
shape of children's games—the whip, the scourge, the rod. Even
the crown of thorns is not forgotten nor the dicing for Christ's
garment. No one has explained to the children the significance
of this ritual, yet, by some seasonal intuition, they recognise March
as the time for these harsh toys and strict competitive games. In
the front playground of the Girls' School the skipping ropes twirl
salt-mustard-vinegar-pepper in a swirl of legs and gym-slips. At
the back, a hundred pairs of hands are keeping a hundred pairs of
tennis balls in continual pat and bounce against the yard wall.
One, two, three and under, one, two, three and over, an upsey, a

F

downsey, a curtsey, a bow, a single decker, a double decker, a
butcher, a baker, a policeman, a rabbit, a thunder:

> Nebuchadnezzar the King of the Jews
> Bought his wife a pair of shoes,
> When the shoes began to wear
> Nebuchadnezzar began to swear,
> When the swear began to stop
> Nebuchadnezzer bought a shop,
> When the shop began to sell
> Nebuchadnezzar bought a bell,
> When the bell began to ring
> Nebuchadnezzar began to sing:
> Doh Ray Me Fah Soh La Te Doh—out.

In the Boys' School there is a fierce Eisteddfod of marbles, and
each dinner-hour the boys run home at the crouch, chasing a
spate of Minties, Poppies, Glassies, and Tullies down the groove
of the gutter. Even in the new housing estates on the far side of
Old Odborough, a boy no higher than the whip he holds is trying
to coax and bully a huge fat top as if he were teaching a puppy to
beg. The top, spun off from his hands, makes a few lazy turns
and wobbles slowly over on to its side, while the boy batters it in
exasperation with the wooden stick of his whip. On a broken
lost pavement, close beneath the slag-bank, Diane Huggins,
Daphne's younger sister, off-school with ring-worm, practises her
way through the complicated changes of hopscotch.

.   .   .

The hours blow onwards, and now the word goes round that
the tide is high at Oatrigg. Timothy Tyson takes out his boolie
early in the afternoon and sets off to have a look. The boolie, an
iron hoop forged by his uncle, Tank Tyson, who works at the
foundry, is smaller than that owned by most boys. In fact, it is
only about a foot across, though rather heavy for its size, so that
its balance is more than usually firm and it bounces over almost
any obstacle barring a brick wall. Timothy does not bowl it with
a stick, as the girls do with their wooden hoops. Instead, he
propels it with a skidder or small iron crook held just an inch or
two above the ground. Sometimes he will go for many yards

without taking the crook away from the boolie, but often he will leave it to run on its own beside him, giving only a slight touch of the crook when it veers off-course.

He trots now through the town, up St Kentigern's Terrace and across the Market Square to the entrance to the footpath which runs along the line-side to the Oatrigg Road. The gale which all night blew in violent gusts, is steadier now, and comes green as plankton, straight from the Irish Sea, scouring the sky. The railway lines glow as if they were oiled, and the telegraph wires sing like larks.

Even the tussocks of last year's grass have a sheen on them. On the slopes of the railway cutting, where they have been burning the dead turf, those which have escaped the fire spike up steely-green in the charred ground. While among the smuts, the silver-gilt of colts-foot glints metallically. In the sump behind the railway turn-table the willows, twisting among old buckets and bent iron rods, prick up a thousand furry ears. Everywhere the birds are busy. There is a whirr and twitter from each hedge; the great tits are sharpening their saws and the starlings boiling their kettles. In the little garth behind the cricket field a few lambs are lying on the sodden ground as if trying to shelter from the wind behind blades of grass.

Timothy Tyson steers his boolie between the two iron railings that cage in this path on the edge of the railway cutting. Carefully he restrains the hoop like a dog on a leach, as he passes prams, boys on bicycles, old ladies with shopping-baskets. Then, coming to the entrance to Jubilee Fields, he stops for a moment to examine where, from what seems to him a life-time of springs he has always found the first celandines. There are dozens now gleaming in the sun, their tinny yellow looking as if it would scrape off. Beside them are the leaves of lords-and-ladies or wild arum, rolled as a child rolls a sheet of paper to make a toy trumpet. And round about are many other plants which older eyes than his would have no difficulty in naming: the smoky-green crumpled lace frills of rough chervil; the pond-weed-like streamers of goose-grass; a little town-clock of moschatel, its four dials facing to the four winds with an extra one facing the sky for the birds to tell the time.

Young Tyson leaves the footpath and enters the main Oatrigg road.   Now he can let his boolie run free.   He tears after it, keen as a hound on the scent.   The air roars about his head, the black hedges are whistling, the buses blow past in a gust of red—but he is blind to them all.   There are other boys about now, hurrying from Old Odborough to see the tide.   The wind is loud with the clatter of shouting, boot-nails, thrushes, and bicycle bells.   Timothy Tyson chases after his flying world, past the few houses, each looking as if it had been snapped off the end of a town terrace like a chunk off a bar of chocolate, and dropped slap-bang on the edge of the road.   This is a district not suburban but sub-rural. There is none of the fancy-dress of the well-to-do residential area, nothing of the sham bucolics of the garden city.   The one or two houses, the bus-stop, the brick urinal, all belong unashamedly to the town.   But the fields behind them are quite uncompromised. They take no notice.   They do not even bother to look pretty, but remain that bare, utilitarian kind of countryside which never gets into the photographs.

Timothy reaches the top of the last low ridge before the coast and lets his boolie free-wheel down into Oatrigg.   It is a pup of Odborough, a village invented by the mines—a scatter of company-owned terraces and of small, bow-windowed villas. Yet it does not look as if it belonged to the mines but only to the sea.

And today the sea is claiming its own.   The wind which all night blew from the north-west, banking up the water on the far side of the estuary, has now veered to the south-west, and is driving the tide across the threshold of the village.   The Oatrigg Pool—which because of the freak of the Ice Age carries all the drainage of the south side of Black Fell—is dammed back by the tide and has overflowed on to the road.   There is a crowd of Odborough boys at the edge of the water.   A hundred yards away, by the Primitive Methodist Chapel, where the tide is held by a rise in the road, Oatrigg boys wave and jeer.   Some of the Odborough tribe try to dash through the flood on bicycles, unaware of the little dip that lies opposite the Pool-side cottages. They advance, their spokes churning the water like the paddles of a river steamer, when, suddenly, the front wheels nose downward and the pedals slap into the water. They brake, and find themselves skimming along like ducks. They cannot turn, cannot put out a foot to gain their balance. Desperately they clutch at the railings at the side of the road and hang there like shipwrecked sailors. The ranks of Tuscany cannot forbear to cheer. Others, climbing on the middle rung of the railings, side-step along until they are poised on stilts above the broadest stretch of the water. A car coming round the corner, refuses as a horse refuses a jump, and turns back again. A hearse makes its way down Harbour Street, while those mourners who come late, raise their hats on the other side of the tide. At the doors of the Poolside cottages, wives and grandfathers watch the tide sniffing around the gates of their small gardens. The bottom of nearly every gate is sealed with sandbags and clay, so that little can seep through, but where the householder has not taken this precaution, the water is wriggling up the shingle of the path. Already one or two women are beginning to block up the bottom of the front door. They are not unduly anxious, however, for there is no real tide here, only the back-flowing of the Pool. But beyond the Primitive Methodist Chapel, in Sea View and Marine Terrace, the sea really does invade the streets. There many a man, fighting with brush and bucket to keep the tide out of his back-yard, has turned to find it rippling through the kitchen, having entered the house by the front door.

Here old Sam Burrows caught a fluke in the parlour and Bill Salt, the fisherman, dug his bait off the front-room oilcloth. Here the ducks have been seen swimming in and out of the *Harbour Hotel*, and the landlord swears he found a plover's egg in the straw of the spittoon. Violet Moss's mother, who was born at Oatrigg, remembers how her father had bailed water out of the pianola. The people of these houses are as wary of the sea as their ancestors were of the Scots. They are ready at any hour to bolt themselves in their pele towers and board up doors and gateways. The yard doors have a double flap, at the bottom, which can be stuffed with clay or sacking. The front gardens often have a boarded fence over which you have to step as over a low stile. All the men and women of this little Holland know the tide-tables off by heart. They can estimate to an inch the combined effect of a high tide and a westerly wind. They have much experience of soaked carpets, damp and slime in the walls, and the floors a wet, stinking slush of salt, sand, scum, oil, tar, shells, weed, and bladder-wrack. Yet someone is caught out every time; someone has forgotten or been lazy or has not noticed the direction of the wind. This is the hope that draw neighbours as the hope of a crash draws crowds to a speed track. The lovely, preposterous catastrophe brings heads to every window and a rush of small boys in Wellingtons wading down the thrust of the tide. A pram stands above the wheel-tops in the water, while the baby leans over the side and grabs at floating feathers. The news tom-toms round the village : ' Ma Bosanco has had it in. Bloody great crabs as big as tortoises walking round the kitchen. She wouldn't come downstairs till we'd thrown her a pair of clogs up to the bedroom window.'

The sea rolls up in a bludgeoning swell, continually skirmished by the wind. Because of the curve of the foreshore, the waves approach it at two angles, and each pair of waves, meeting, amalgamates into a bore that pushes along the channel of the Pool, and then—at the same point every time—leaps the rails into the streets. The water froths against the slate porches of the chapel, and the freestone doorsteps and low window-sills, and concrete slabs of the Company terraces. Gulls rock like buoys in the centre of the street and oyster-catchers skirl past only a foot above the dogs that are chasing them in a frenzy of frustration. The highest swells are lifting over the rise by the chapel and trickling into Harbour Square. Give it another six inches, and two-thirds of the village will be flooded in no time. But already the tide is on the turn. The ripples no longer reach to the limit of the wet. The water slinks back into the Pool. The houses stand ugly and unconcerned as ever, their feet in a tide-mark of slop and wrack and rubbish. The sun gives the wet streets the dazzle of tinfoil. The dumped sand, drying quickly, is whipped up by the wind into a brown, gritty smother. The cats return to the pavements. And Timothy Tyson stirs up his boolie and trundles back home.

.   .   .

When the light lengthens in March it is as if a door had been unlocked. Violet Moss stands on the outside of that door, more than half afraid to push it open.

It is the night of the Vernal Equinox. She has been to Confirmation Class and is returning circuitously by the Jubilee Fields.

The astringent breeze of Lent is blowing across her face. The pancakes of Shrove Tuesday and the hash of Ash Wednesday are now as distant as Christmas Cake, and the willows are fluffy with Palm Sunday palm. It was bright evening when she left St Kentigern's, but now the day is ebbing fast. A misty mauve washes over the sky, except westward, where still it is green and the thorn-trees are sharply black against it. The church spire is blurred against the darker east. From here the town is entirely hidden by the Jubilee Hill, while the fallow fields that slope up to the churchyard wall are as empty as the fell-tops. Farther off, the smaller slag-bank humps itself into the dusk—an ancient animal shape that seems now indigenous to the landscape, having more right to be there than the town ever had. Everywhere the rock heaves to be free of the soil—you can see the pull and strain in the creases of the furrows. In the carboniferous twilight the limestone returns to life. The stone walls are coral reefs. The fossils creep out of their holes and swarm across the landscape. The warm mauve seas wash smoothly over the lagoons of evening.

Violet Moss stands dead still. She has no knowledge of the life within the rocks, yet in that primitive part of her mind which is as old as the fossils, she recognises all that she does not see, and understands all that she does not know. Ammonites and belemnites are her contemporaries and companions : the salt mauve tides rise in her blood. She feels the pressure in her temples. The sky flows with purple; the grass of the field is slack as seaweed. The thrushes are ceasing to sing, and blackbirds clatter among the dark hawthorns.   She feels Easter looming up before her, big as the slag-bank.   She thinks of her first communion almost with terror.   She feels the strain of the growing grass.   All that is to come, in school, home, sex, and work, seems part of the labour and thrust of spring.   The dark purple mists swirl and settle, smudging shapes of tree and wall and slag-bank.   The Market Clock strikes eight, the church bells begin their mid-week practice, and Violet sets off, half-running, towards home.

April

DAFFODILS HAVE a time-table of their own in Odborough. In January they appear only in wreaths, sickly and dying among the evergreen. In February they are seen in shops and parlour windows, making little splashes of sulphur all along the grey of the street. In March they begin to shoot up in orchards. A shudder of yellow runs under the apple-trees and the washing whenever the wind blows. But April is the month for the garden narcissi. Then they bounce and see-saw in every allotment and lawn—yellow trumpets and white, large cups and small ones, bunch-flowered and doubles—Pheasant's Eye, Cheerfulness, Beersheba, Scarlet Elegance, Texas, King Alfred, and Mrs E. H. Krelage. They stand, now, on this Good Friday, in the churchyard beside the drive, in garden-party clothes, dithering in the cool wind. The yellow orchard daffodils warm the breath like brandy, but these make you cold to look at them. The season is not ready and we are not ready for the season.

Nor are we ready for Easter. One may say that no one can be

ready for Easter who has not lived through Lent, just as a bulb cannot be ready for the spring if it has not lived through winter. The Protestant world scarcely knows how to celebrate Good Friday. One might have thought that a religion which bases itself on the Atonement would have made Good Friday the central day of its year. And, indeed, a Methodist Chapel at a small village near Odborough used to hold its Sunday School Anniversary on that day, with a picnic tea in the field outside and children's games among the rocks. But as the doctrine of the Atonement began to give way to the cult of the Good Samaritan, so Good Friday declined from a day of rejoicing or of mourning to a mid-week Sunday with a United Free Church service in the evening. Even the Church of England, which, in practice, may be defined as a catholic church with a protestant congregation, sometimes finds Good Friday almost an embarrassment. Holy sorrow has no longer its place in religion. However gloomy men may be during the week, they are optimistic on Sunday. They base their faith on the Sermon on the Mount. Blessed are the comfortable, for they shall obtain comfort. The Crucifixion is now an unnecessary extravagance.

So it is that the congregation which walks up the Church Drive between the daffodils for the last hour of the Three-hour Service is the smallest at any major festival of the year. Two weeks before, the church had been packed to the door for the Confirmation, and of those who were confirmed only one is kneeling there now, together with about twenty women and two men. The vicar, in his black cassock, sits on a chair on the chancel steps, holding a few notes on the Seven Last Words. There is no choir, no organ, no sound but the footsteps of the latest comers in the aisle. Canon Olds looks down the church to the west end where the sun pours through the window like water through a grill. It seems incredibly strange, this so familiar building. For only at this one service of the year does the sun itself become a worshipper. At Matins it shines from the east into the sanctuary; at Evensong, in the summer, it shines from the north-west into the nave. But only on this Good Friday service does it enter the church from behind the font and walk down the aisle with the rest of the congregation. Each bowed head bears a chignon of sunlight on the nape. The dull woodwork is varnished with sun. The cat from *The Prince of Wales*, which, like Anna, the prophetess, departs not from the temple night and day, is asleep in a pew on the side aisle and, for once, Canon Olds does not chase her out. The sun wanders about the church as if it belonged there. As, indeed, it does, for the building is the product of the sun, being made of the red desert sandstone which lies beside the slate all along the Cumberland coast. The pillars burn as red as the sand beyond Jordan when the Word was first heard. The stones are bare beneath a hot Messianic sun.

'What went ye out into the wilderness for to see?' asks the vicar in the words of Another: Violet Moss, uneasy on her thin knees; the two younger Miss Snoots who have quarrelled with the eldest and are living in lodgings in Rotting Road; Mrs Quorum, who in her mind is decorating the lectern with the red tulips she has brought for that purpose. The sound blows and billows about their heads, in spirals and arches and whirlwinds.

Canon Olds stands, a voice crying in the desert. But there will be none else to hear, he thinks, none else now. He kneels and begins The Lord's Prayer.

.   .   .

But not quite none. In the porch stands Derek Dale, third-year English (Hons.) student at Sheffield University, grandson to Tommy Dale and reluctant heir to Late Cheap and Best. Good Friday means a great deal to Derek Dale, for he is an atheist. Three years ago, when he declared his unbelief and refused to attend chapel, atheism had seemed a manifesto of liberty. But after eight terms among a generation too unaccustomed to belief even to deny it, he finds himself restless as a convict in a prison-without-bars with nowhere to escape from. So that now, on his return to Odborough, he begins to relish all signs of the faith he does not hold. He has become a visitor of country churches, an eavesdropper at midday communions, and a secret reader of *The War Cry*. On Sunday mornings, from above his grandfather's shop, he watches the hundreds hurrying to Mass at St Joseph's,

and would have followed them and spied them through a crack
in the window did he not know that he would end up in Rotting
Pool if he were caught.   On Sunday evenings he watches the
half-dozen or so trickling to the various Methodist Chapels and
smiles in perverse satisfaction at the shut cinemas, the chained
swings in the Jubilee Pleasure Ground, and the blue-serge shuffle
at the street corner.   He is, he suspects, the only declared agnostic
in England who subscribes to the Lord's Day Observance Society.
For he is disgusted with those who think such things do not matter.
He wishes he could have been born in age of faith—a secret
Protestant in the Spain of the Inquisition, or a secret Catholic in
John Knox's Scotland.   In the Middle Ages, for instance, he
might have been a witch, or a renegade priest at the Black Mass,
practising obscene perversions and defiances.   It would have
needed courage, then, to refuse to acknowledge his own damna-
tion.   But, today, even blasphemy is no more than picturesque.
He strains forward to the door, hearing only a mumble.
   ' Lord, I do not believe,' he mutters to himself.   ' Help Thou
mine unbelief.'
   He leaves the porch and walks past the heliotrope jungle of
rhubarb leaves to the graveyard at the top of the hill.   Here, on
a drumlin of clay left by the Ice Age, the dead lie higher than anyone else in the parish.   He looks with approval at the Victorian
tombstones, which may lack the lugubrious lament of the eighteenth century in Odborough Old Church, but have at least a
relevance in their words and emblems.   They do not decline into
the doctrinal non-committance of the modern memorials with
their plain stone crosses like the signs of Spiritual First Aid, and
their continually optimistic mottoes : ' At Rest ', ' Till We Meet
Again '.   And why the devil, says Derek Dale to himself, do they
always put them in inverted commas?
   He moves along the path between the graves—many of them
already wearing their Easter wreaths.   Behind him lies the town.
At his back and to the left, the Ironworks; at his back and to the
right, the railway and the cricket field, where, he notices with
regret, a group of men are preparing for the next season.   He
comes now to the end of the graveyard, climbs over the high wall,

and at once is many miles away.   It is true, that, away to his left
he can still see the mines, and away to his right the houses of Old
Odborough.   But straight ahead of him the eye slips out of the
grasp of the town as the dead slip out of the grasp of life here on
this hill.   Released like a whippet, the vision streaks down the
slope of the green, leaps across path and hedge, chases its tail in
the meadows, jumps clean over buses on the Oatrigg road, and
tears away straight to the sea until young Dale whistles it back.

This is a countryside without a beauty to its name, so that the
town has turned its back, and the little suburban houses have gone
nosing off the other way towards the woods and the prospects.
The one or two buildings between here and Oatrigg have been
dumped by the roadside without a thought for siting or design,
with the result that their accidental ugliness never obtrudes itself
on your notice.   There are no views to speak of.   No trees, no
rocks, no river, no cottages.   Nothing is on show.   The season
goes about its business without the least self-consciousness.   The
hedges are in shirt-sleeves; the muck heaps do not excuse themselves; the birds have not learned to beg.   This is a landscape
that looks and feels and smells not like a view but like grass and
soil and stones.

Derek Dale sits now on one of those stones with his back to the
churchyard wall.   His hand is pleasantly tingling with the first
nettle-sting of the year.   Beside him, on the ground, Dr Leavis
on George Eliot covers a half-dozen daisies—which should make
it spring, if Leavis on Eliot counts as much as a boot.   Yet spring
is approaching as if by stealth.   The wind creeps up under cover
of a dark-green mist that encircles the scene like a barb-wire
entanglement.   The chimney-stacks and old pit-heads of the
mines catch the sun just within the pale, but the estuary and the
sea and the fells are all blanketed out.   The sun seeps down as if
through muslin.   Every grass blade—short new-green and longer
old-grey—has a fuzz of sheen, brilliant on the southward slope of
an old furrow, and dull or shadowed on the northward slope.
The rut-weeds are loosening their collars—speedwell and buttercup and lady's smock.   The hedges show everywhere a wash of
green, faint where thorns have caught the biting wind, but thick

and heavy where elder and gooseberry are mingled with the willows.   Here and there the black sticks are chalked with sloe-blossom, and whin bushes, piled in wave upon wave against a wall, are crested and flecked with yellow.   Sun and wind seem to contradict one another, as if there were two different weathers at one time.   A chaffinch shakes its dice box and throws out the dice—ping ping—on a little tin tray.   A willow wren, still surprised to be in England, tinkles out a few interrogative notes.   The larks are shrill.   The air is sharp as a lemon.   To those who have not acquired a taste for it, April can set the teeth on edge.

.   .   .

Derek Dale tightens his windjammer jacket and stares down the hill to the Jubilee Fields.   The after-dinner walks are beginning : young couples and middle-aged.   The middle-aged pairs will continue to make the circuit until their legs are too old to carry them, but for the young, the country walk will end with marriage.   Once, the people of Odborough had known every lane and path for miles around.   They would visit each at the right season—a favourite primrose patch or a holly bush as if it were an old friend.   During the slump the out-of-work iron men would spend hours on the Tops looking across the unsmoking chimneys to the estuary, or gathering mushrooms and blackberries and bits of sticks for firewood.   Dole diet may have taken the red from their cheeks, but not the strength from their legs.   Today the Tops are empty and the field-paths greened over.   The better-off circumnavigate the district in cars, but the young workers are oblivious to the country.   They think of themselves as townsmen and turn to scratchy imitations of the townsman's pleasures.   Their girls try to dress like town girls, and display all the badges of the pavement parade—high heels, ear-rings, hand-bags, and cheap scent.   The town girl does not enjoy privacy; she plays, as she works, in public.   And after marriage there is enough privacy in kitchen or in bed and no need to search for it in the lanes or behind hedges.   But for this one period of courtship, when the street is too public and the home too private, the couples break from their flock like nesting chaffinches and spread out among

the fields. They explore the spots their parents talk about—
Odborough Pier, Oatrigg Dunes, the Castle Woods, and along
the estuary and up into the hills. In two or three years their
walks will cease, but they will carry memories of those places into
their old age. And maybe one day, doing the honours to a
grandson or a visitor, they will re-inspect the landscape of memory
and find that time has either erased it or preserved it neat and
green as a pickled onion.

They are sauntering now among the budding bread-and-cheese,
with never a suspicion that it is what they pay no notice to that
they will remember the most poignantly—the lark song, the lamb
bleat, the king-cups in the ditch, the blackthorn in the hedge.
Such things, coming without warning before their eyes or into
their ears, will bring back the tingle of courtship more palpably
than a midnight of willed recollections.

' Oh,' she says, pointing among the celandines, ' a bee.'

And he does not even notice the celandines, but the bee has left
its buzz in his memory for ever.

.   .   .

Councillor Quorum does not notice the bee either, and ascribes
the girl's sudden start to quite another cause. He has been
watching the couple for some time, and stands at the top of the
hill leaning over the railings of the Jubilee Pleasure Ground, a pair
of binoculars hanging from a leather lace round his neck. He
finds these binoculars very useful in carrying out his council
duties. By their aid from the distance, he was able to scrutinise
the Oatrigg Rocks at high tide, thereby coming to the conclusion
that facilities for changing were needed by the bathers. In the
case of the Jubilee Fields he is specially interested in the public
seat which the couple has just left. Councillor Quorum is under
the conviction that the position of this seat is Unsuitable, leading
to the embarrassment of town's people using the footpath. His
binoculars have done much to strengthen this conviction and to
increase the embarrassment. The couple move away, and the
Councillor turns and walks across the miniature golf-course
towards the Old Age Pensioners' Summer Club.

At least, this was what he hopes it will be called in next week's issue of *The Odborough Gazette*. In fact, it is the shed where the lawn mower and the deck-chairs are kept during the winter. These latter are now piled outside on the green, together with the folding chairs waiting for a coat of paint, and it has been the Councillor's idea that the hut should be cleaned out and made available for the old folk. The cleaning has not been over-conscientious, but a coke stove has been fitted, together with a table and a couple of forms, and the Councillor himself has kindly donated a second-hand domino set and six new packs of cards stamped ' Odborough O.A.P.' in purple ink. Today is Opening Day, and already half a dozen old men have arrived, and those who are not winded by climbing up the hill are busy fumigating the hut with a strong smirch of twist. Almost all of them were born in the town, and the day when the Jubilee Hill earned its name is clearer than yesterday in their eyes. One, who had been a fast bowler when Odborough first won the League in 1895, walks now in a forward bend as if he were perpetually delivering the ball that won the last match. One, who is almost blind, had been billiards champion year after year, and spends his summer watching clumsy cannons and kisses on the baize of the bowling green. Yet another had played the euphonium in the Odborough Temperance Band at that garden fête in which the Prince had written ' Royal ' in chalk across the big bass drum.

The Old Age Pensioners' Association, to whom they all belong, is now one of the most flourishing societies in Odborough. Every year it grows, for more people age and fewer die. Like the teen-agers—that other group on the edge of adulthood—the old feel united merely because they belong to the same generation. Differences of sect, opinion, and interests which separated them between the ages of twenty and seventy now seem to matter very little, so that while those of ordinary middle life are divided and at loggerheads, the old and the young are united and agreed. It is the young who make the most noise and attract the most atten-tion, but it is the old who are more sure of themselves. The young, in any case, are as yet a generation of nobodies. If they are known at all, it is because of the names of their fathers, and as soon as one of them makes a name for himself he ceases, in a way, to be young. The old, however, will not cease to be old. They are all life members of their generation and will never lack recruits. They are the new leisured class, poor as the unemployed, but with none of their hopelessness and bitterness. Many of them are still as active as they have ever been. They have their weekly whist drives, their monthly concerts. They have a bus outing to the Lakes or the shore in summer, and the crowning of an Autumn Queen at Christmas. Every now and then the cinema gives them a free matinée, and once a year the Rotarians take them in private cars for tea at a country inn with a concert afterwards. For some while they have been subscribing a penny a week to build or buy a clubroom, but not all of them can afford to wait until this is achieved. For such men—widowers living with married daughters, refugees from scrubbing and grandchildren—the hut provides at least an alternative to the public library, with only a little less comfort and with no restrictions on natural and unavoidable noises.

They sit now, in a fume of tobacco, paraffin, and turpentine, staring without seeing through the open door. April makes demands too harsh for old eyes. The town is brittle, bright, and angular as a handful of crystals. Slate roofs are green and pointed, and the ventilators of Rotting Road School jut up like newly sharpened pencils. The light is bright again, but as heartless as schoolgirls. There is not a blur of haze or a shimmer of shadow over the walls. Every stone stands clear, every crack or stain or crumbling of concrete. The chimneys are as bare as the sycamores in the churchyard, and the blotched brick-ends of the Public Library thrust themselves into notice like children displaying their sores. It is as if the whole town were under inspection by the clinical light, and half fears that it will be condemned.

The old men moderate the atmosphere with their pipes and muse into the comfort of winter.

.   .   .

G

John Dodder—who is having one of his better days—sits propped up in a chair by the window. In the Pleasure Ground he can see the caretaker painting the tramlines on the tennis courts which open on Easter Monday. For a few weeks the courts will be crowded—one will have to queue or book hours ahead to be sure of a game. Young girls, who last year were still entangled in hopscotch and skipping, will present themselves, eager as debutantes, and though their enthusiasm will not last beyond midsummer, it will give to the spring evenings a trilling of giggles to blend with the throstles. In the allotments a few men are turning over the soil, or refilling flower-pots and seed-boxes. Others—following a stubborn theory that is disproved every year —are planting potatoes. There is a spangle of green in the currant bushes, and the ridges of the dug ground twang with light like the strings of a strummed banjo.

But John Dodder is not concerned with these. Instead, he leans forward as far as he can, and gazes down into the road below. Today a new season's hatching of girls is coming out. He recognises scarcely one of them, for a year ago they were indistinguishable to a man's eyes in a scuffle of scarves and cardigans, while all through the winter they have been hidden away in factory or office or VIth Form. They emerge now on bicycles, bright sweaters repeating the shape of the handlebars. They crouch forward or stand on the pedals, swinging the machines as if they were mettlesome horses; legs, stripped as for the Folies Bergères, thrust downwards with the force of pile-drivers. They wheel and swerve and look back over their shoulders, with not even a glance, seemingly, at where they are going. Blue shorts swivel on a saddle, and a toe, stretched out like an oar, kicks the edge of the kerbstone. There is a blow-about of hair and half-unbuttoned blouses, and the wind wriggles its fingers almost where it pleases. Young men's voices ricochet harmlessly off bare arms and the bicycle bells screech in invitation.

John Dodder blinks his eyes, dazzled but unresentful. This is not his generation. It is not just injury which holds him back. If he had the body of Tarzan he could no more find a word to say to these girls than he can now. For such as him, for such as

Councillor Quorum, for such as every blessed man in Odborough old enough to remember Shirley Temple, this is a treat for the eyes only. With an impulse that he can hardly recognise, he thanks God for his eyes.

.   .   .

The girls swing round the corner into St Kentigern's Terrace, through the Market Square, over the Railway Bridge, and for once they do not turn back. On weekday evenings throughout the summer they will wheel about on their hire-purchased cycles, circling the town as the swifts circle the Market Clock. They will pass and re-pass up and down the streets, yet rarely will they adventure even a yard beyond the last houses. On Sundays and Good Friday, however, they will run out to Oatrigg or along the Black Fell valley, or, in summer, to the shore at Sallowcroft, three miles up the coast.

They pass the Wreck now, in a jingle and neighing, and wave to the men in the cricket field without bothering to notice who they are. Tank Tyson, bending over a pail of whitewash, does not manage to straighten himself in time to wave back. This is one of the days when the few working members of the committee are able to get busy on the field. Tank Tyson slaps the whitewash on the boards, splashing an abundance of daisies round about. Though, like the rest of the members present, the Tank is middle-aged—the young ones will not turn up till the work is over and the season begun—he is still able to hold his place in the First Eleven. But he likes to do his fielding in the slips and his whitewashing at eye-level. So he straightens himself once again and watches the girls now careering down the Oatrigg road, the width of two fields away. He envies them. Except for the labour of cycling. The country is a good place when you are young. It is a pity that his nephew doesn't see more of it, instead of sitting all day with his nose in a book or being dragged off to chapel by his sanctimonious old grandfather.

.   .   .

But in this he is mistaken. Old Mr Sprout is not taking Timothy to chapel. For like many Nonconformists, Mr Sprout gives little thought to any festival but the Sabbath. He has no sense of the Ecclesiastical Year, though he has a great sense of the Ecclesiastical Week. Even Christmas Day, when it falls on Monday to Saturday, is no more to him than a mid-winter Bank Holiday, and when it does fall on a Sunday he keeps it as a Sunday, making his children put away their toys and wait till Boxing Day for their presents. Or so he did when they were little.

Today, therefore, he is taking his grandson not to chapel but for a walk along the Dunner Banking. They are leaving Railway Road now, and passing through the little tunnel under the Iron-works branch line. In front, the saltings and sands reach to Furness, but there is no sign of the sea, for the peninsula of Odborough New Town stretches half-way across the mouth of the river, blotting out the western horizon, with slag-banks and chimneys. From the summit of Scafell and Coniston Old Man the Ironworks can be seen sailing out into the estuary like a great battleship, smoking at all funnels. This decayed edge of the marsh, wedged between the gas-works and the Dunner Banking, seems to belong neither to the land nor to the sea. The tide arrives only three or four times a year, and in summer it is burnt dry as concrete. Yet the salt has laid its savour here, and the smell is the smell of rotting seaweed, fish, and the excrement of sea-birds. At the bottom of the railway embankment it is the salt plants that grow among the pumice-like crumbles of washed-up slag—sea plantain, sea purslane, sea milkwort, and thrift. The mud flats are mauve and brown, not yet responding to the spring, but in the gulleys the leaves of the scurvy-grass are green as spinach and thickly frosted with white cress-flowers. The tide is rising fast and will be one of the highest of the season. Very little of the marshes is covered as yet, but the water is flowing off the drains, and seeping into the pools and creeks that lie among the turf. The Rotting Pool, which usually runs five or six feet below the surface in its deep moat of mud, is now full almost to the brim, and scum and bubbles and gull's feathers drift upstream on the thrust.

Mr Sprout and Timothy Tyson are crossing the Pool, now, by the old Parish Boundary Bridge, and stepping up to the Dunner

Banking—a twenty-foot-high embankment of rubble and sods that runs for three miles along the side of the estuary. Fifty years ago —before the slag had blotted out the mouth of the river and the smell had oozed into Rotting Pool—this had been the town's promenade. For the first mile, the path along the top is paved with concrete, and at spaces of fifty yards there are benches, set alternately facing outward to the marshes or inward to the hills. Here, in Edwardian years, the shopkeepers walked with their wives, tapping the concrete with the ferrules of their canes, or rested on the benches and hung their bowler hats on the iron lion-heads of the end-brackets. Here prams were parked and families sat on rugs while the children ran barefoot on the turf. Here, at moderate tides, boys would cross the half-mile of flats to the water, and bathe naked under the screen of the shore. And here, too, on Easter Monday was the place for rolling pace-eggs.

It is this latter that Mr Sprout is talking about. As they had passed along Railway Road they had seen the pace-eggs on show in the sash-windows of the terraced houses: hard-boiled eggs stained with cochineal or coffee or vegetable skins. Today many are dyed purple and green and other impossible colours and painted with fancy faces. Mr Sprout has no patience with such-like. He has not given much thought to the religious significance of the eggs. He does not know that the word ' Pace ' is a deriva-tive of ' Paschal ', and he would be astonished to learn that the egg, as a ritual symbol of resurrection, is far older than Chris-tianity. But he has a regard for what is right and proper in such matters, and funny faces, he is convinced, are not. Pace-eggs, he holds, should be dyed with the fruits of the field or garden—with gorse flowers, giving a mellow lemon glow, or with onion skins, marbling the shells with Harvest Festival colours.

When he was a boy, he tells Timothy, he might get as many as a dozen pace-eggs at Easter, but not one was so much as handled until Easter Monday—before then his mother would put them on the window-ledge well out of his reach. Then on the Monday they were taken down and polished and tested with a light tapping of the finger-nail. The two that seemed the frailest were put aside—for his mother insisted that he should leave at least two at

home, in case he lost the rest.   The ten that survived were stuffed
one by one into separate pockets, and immediately after dinner,
off he would go to the Banking.   By one o'clock there would be
hundreds of children there, and, if the day was bright, they would
soon be joined by the parents.   The Band might be out, and one
of the Plymouth Rocks, prophesying to the wind, and old Isaac
Crossthwaite (the founder of the St Kentigern's Temperance
Hotel) with his ice-cream barrow.   He used to serve the ice-
cream in little glasses, but if you were wise you took your own
cup and got a little more.   There would be a hubbub of larking
and frisking and tousling—big lads wrestling on the turf, little girls
in a windmill of ribbons, dogs splashing in the gutters and shaking
themselves dry against the new spring satins and laces.

But the egg-rolling itself was conducted with gravity.   The
place reserved for it was a stretch at the foot of the inside of the
embankment, where the ground had been levelled and the grass
mown.   Some of the children would roll their eggs down the
slope of the turf, but most of them gathered in little groups of five
or six and arranged themselves as for a game of marbles.   The
eggs were then rolled, in pairs, from either side of the ring, towards
the centre.   If, when the eggs clashed together the shells of both
were broken, then each was out of the match and was pocketed by
the owner.   If only one was broken, the winner took both eggs
and went on with his unbroken one to challenge others.   A boy
with two or more eggs of unusual toughness could sometimes win
a couple of dozen.   There were various techniques in rolling.
Some delivered slowly and steadily like bowlers delivering woods
on a bowling green; others believed in a sharp, hard crack at the
opponent.   Older lads stood about to watch fair-play and to deal
with the bullies who refused to surrender broken eggs, while anyone who tried the old trick of using a stained pot-egg was likely to
get ducked in the Rotting Pool.

Timothy looks back apprehensively at that Pool.   A ducking
today would be very nearly a drowning, for the channel is full to
the brim, and so, too, are all the other gullies and canals—the
water lapping over, linking inlet to inlet, broadening the pools,
islanding the nine-inch uplands of the marsh, and spreading in a

lagoon between the Boundary Bridge and the gas-works. Un-noticed, within the time of talking, the sea has retaken possession.

Far out on a hump of the marsh now completely insulated, a few sheep are feeding on a diminishing area of grass—old tups and ewes not due to lamb, which the farmer has forgotten or has not bothered to gather in. Timothy points worriedly to them.

' They'll be all right,' says Mr Sprout. ' Tide'll be on the turn in a minute.'

For all that, he is as worried as his grandson. The path by which they reached the Banking from Railway Road is inundated. The gullies are disappearing and you can no longer trace their course. The two walls of the Boundary Bridge, carrying no road and crossing no beck, rise preposterously from the flats of water.

And now, suddenly, the sheep find that their bank is flooded and the water nearly up to their bellies. Some of them try to escape, but immediately begin to plunge and flounder in the deeper water on the edge of the gullies. The others stay still, and merely raise their heads reluctantly from cropping and begin to baa. The sea is unrippled, grey, dull-shining as pewter. Reflections appear on it blurred but undistorted, like a view seen through a dirty glass window. The whole range of the Ironworks and slag-banks lies upside down on the grey of the water, the posts of the breakwater running up the chimney-stacks like scaffolding. The slag-banks slant down in underwater cliffs or grottoes, and the smoke whirls and whitens as if a school of porpoises were blowing below the waves. What ten minutes ago was an inch or two of dampness, oozing across the marsh, is now a lake as deep as the sky. The tide is alive with the shadows of sea-birds, chasing the real birds three feet above them. Quick black-and-white oyster-catchers and ring plovers are flung out to sea like a handful of pebbles at every turn and flick of the wind. Gulls are few, having already congregated in their colonies among the dunes. Shelduck are in pairs and will soon fly off to the moors. Curlews gargle; peewits creak. An engine on the Ironworks line eases its safety valve, and a jet of pure white steam descends like an inverted whirlpool deep into the depths of the tide.

The sheep now are growing more alarmed, for the water has

mounted their backs and they crane upward with their necks, keeping their heads above the surface. They are baa-ing pitifully, but no longer dare move, for every step threatens to drown them. The dozen or so heads jut out inexplicably above a sea that looks deep enough to swamp the Ironworks chimney-stacks, and the air is filled with the wailing of mermaids. Timothy turns apprehensively to his grandfather.

'No sense in it at all,' says the old man. 'They should never have been left out in these tides. No sense in it at all.'

.   .   .

Bogey Burrows is watching the sheep, too, but less apprehensively. He has seen it happen many times before. Besides, the tide is already on the turn. From his look-out perched high up on the slag-bank he can see signs that are not noticed by those below : the birds flying farther off the land; the shading of the water as the rushes begin to appear through it; and the current of the gullies making itself visible once again on the surface of the water like a faint smear seen through the bottom of a glass tumbler.

In twenty years Bogey has had the job of foreman on the tip (with the finest view, he says, from any slag-bank in England), and no one in Odborough knows more of the countryside round about. Not that he ever sets foot in it. The cricket field in summer and the Working Men's in winter are as far as he ever goes, but he can tell you the crop of every field on either side of the estuary. He knows, to an hour, when each farmer begins ploughing or haymaking and when the fishermen are out or the duck-shooters or the hounds. He watches the bracken burning on the Tops in late spring, and times each orchard as it bursts into blossom, and spots any new barn or cottage before the walls are three foot high. From his hut in a corrie of the bank, he sees where the duck fly off in pairs to nest and he watches the geese congregate in October, and is acquainted with the movements of heron and cormorant and the time-table of the owls. He has known swans, moorhen, coot, and duck of a dozen kinds nest in the furnace reservoir, and watched the pipit rear a cuckoo in the whins behind the pier, and threatened to get the sack for any man

who touched it.   He knows the estuary better than the pilot, and
when the salmon are running he will scan the pools with his
binoculars as the tide ebbs and will pass on the news to his friends
the MacIntyre Brothers.   One of them, caught wheeling a ten-
pound salmon off the Dunner Banking in a perambulator was
brought up in Court and fined forty shillings.   Afterwards, in
The Prince of Wales, the magistrate quietly handed him two
pounds in a sealed envelope.

('And so he bloody well should have,' says Chunker Wilson.
'It was him that got the salmon.')

Bogey turns his back on the estuary and gazes across the fields
that lie between the Ironworks and the Mines.   All through the
willows by the reservoir the wind blows shiverings of green.   The
white poplars in the gravel patch behind the water-tank shine like
new aluminium, and at the foot of the slag-bank the horsetails
prick up their brown periscopes to see if it is time for the fronds
to come out.

This afternoon, however, Bogey Burrows is not concerned with
the landscape.   He is looking, instead, at the field below Limestone Hill where the Ironworks Sports Club are playing the first
round of the Rugby League Seven-a-Side knock-out.   For this is
the last great football week-end of the winter.   All up and down
the towns of England crowds are gathered to watch the game, and
here, in Odborough, small groups are gathered to play it.   Bogey
can see four of them spread about the field between Odborough
and Oatrigg, each with its straggle of spectators.   As the wind
shifts and rallies, a faint sound of cheering drifts up from one or
other of the matches, and referees' whistles compete with the
willow wrens.   Every now and then a ball soars into the air and
a linesman chases it, jerking his flag.   A scrimmage of white and
red or blue is blown about, as if without purpose, among the gusty
green.   The spectators do not move, or at most, wave stick-like
arms, anonymous as the inhabitants of a Lowry drawing, while
the green air of April washes around and over them, swilling turf
and goal and hedge and slag and mine and road and wall and
roof and shop and square and church and hill and sea.   The
clock strikes four.

The Miss Snoots sit down, in all the resentment of punctuality, to a not-yet-ready lodger's tea. Violet Moss, coming through the Jubilee Fields as usual on her way home, meets Derek Dale, down-stepping through the daisies. The bicycle girls, returning from Oatrigg, meet younger boys, returning from the Dunner, with bunches and bunches of wild daffodils—tiny, pale flowers, tied to the cross-bar or strung like Spanish onions on a stick cut from the hedge. Mr Sprout and Timothy pick their way back across the wet footpath towards Railway Road. Tank Tyson waves a whitewash brush at the football followers crossing the Bridge.

'No time for rugby now,' he calls out. 'You're living in the past.'

The Old Age Pensioners disperse for tea.

May

I HAVE OFTEN thought that the National Trust ought to preserve some typical examples of the landscape created and shaped by industry and then deserted : abandoned ironworks and slag-banks, old clay pits, old quarries, old lead workings, decayed ports and wharves, brick-fields, gravel-pits, broken-down factories and warehouses, derelict collieries, and worked-out iron-ore mines. It is not just that all such places have an obvious romantic charm, with their reminder of mortality and of the vanity of human wishes. It is rather that they give a glimpse beyond the scale of history; they set man in the greater perspective of biology and geology, of the pre-historic and post-historic processes of nature. Here, in the flashes among the slag-banks, or in the rubble-heaps of collieries, we can see nature fighting back, re-colonising the former enemy-occupied territory. It is not a ruin, but a renaissance.

And of all these types of industrial landscape, that of the iron-ore mines is by far the most agreeable both to the eye and to the nose. There is no dirt about iron-ore. It comes to the surface in clean lumps, about the colour and size of a pickle cabbage. It has neither the deadness of slag nor the grime of coal. In many ways iron-mining is very like agriculture—a root crop, deeply dug, the harvest of which is stored like huge clamps of turnips or mangold wurzels. But it is a crop that exhausts. After the first gathering the land lies fallow for ever.

The iron-mines of Odborough have been among the most famous in the world, producing haematite ore from an almost unbelievably rich deposit. The men who opened the mines had no idea of the wealth which awaited them. For centuries it had been noticed that there were smudges of red among the limestone rocks at Odborough Point, and farmer had made use of the red clay to mark the backs of their sheep. Then about the 1850s a company was formed to sink a small shaft to mine the ore. The deposit was discovered to be larger than had been expected. Other shafts were sunk and other pits opened—all named after members of the firm : ' George Pit ', ' Brougham Pit ', and ' Mary Annie Lonsdale '. The town began to grow. The Ironworks were established. A sea-wall was built, and gradually it became evident that great deposits of ore lay under the sea, between levels of high and low water. Finally, about the beginning of the century, a huge barrier was built to keep out the tide, and a new parish was added to England.

As the century advanced the ore receded. One after one the earlier pits were closed and new ones opened nearer the Oatrigg end of the sea-wall. Water began to seep into the old workings, carrying sand with it as in a fluid, underground glacier. The land subsided. Houses collapsed; roads caved in; a railway loco-motive dived out of sight into a hole which opened for it like a yawn. Fields round about sagged like underdone pie-crusts. The output of the mine declined, many of the men were paid off, and new industries were set up to give them work. Today only a few score are employed by the mine, and it is hard to remember how the town was once entirely dependent on it, being rooted in the rock as firmly as a tree. It is hard to realise that when the water broke into the mine, the whole town cringed under the threat of catastrophe. It is hard to understand how, in my own family, the memory of my Uncle Jack, killed in an underground fall years before I was born, remained as that of a hero, a pioneer. The mines do not obtrude, being hidden on their lost peninsula well out of sight of the town. You can live for years in one of the housing estates of the new Odborough without even noticing them. Yet here in the hollow of the mines is the womb from which the town was born, and from the red of the ore came the blood transfusion which brought new life to this once barren coast.

It is the red that first catches the eye. The earth seems drenched with it. The paths are red; the rabbit-holes are red. The rubble-tips beside the old workings rise in huge red screes. The becks and drains run red as blood in their limestone culverts, and the willows beside them seem so soaked in the colour that you would expect them to ooze red when plucked, like the trees in Dante's Wood of Suicides. Wooden huts and fencing and pit-head gear are stained darker than mahogany, and on the railway lines dark-red sleepers are set in dark-red ballast.

Yet it is not primarily a sombre landscape. Indeed, it might have been planned by some mid-Victorian Capability Brown just to amuse the eye. The old pits are arranged with an elegance which is almost affected—chimney-stacks, shaft-heads, pit-wheels, grouped against the sky. The little railways rush up and down like a switchback, figure-eighting round the old shafts, leaping across clefts in the rock, skirting quarries, skittling over rickety viaducts, sliding under bridges and through tunnels. Narrow-gauge lines for hand-bogeys jut out on scaffolding from the pit-heads and break off in mid-air like a high-diving board. Everywhere, lying about, there is a gigantic bric-à-brac of iron—fallen pylons; rusted girders; cog-wheels cluttered in bramble; wagons left there so long that the store-man keeps hens in them; and enough scrap to build a battleship.

The pits were opened one after another along the edge of an escarpment that slopes down to what used to be the foreshore. It slopes, in fact, farther than it did before, for the land has sub-sided below sea-level, and the first sea-wall has foundered till it seems like a sinking ship, forever about to be engulfed by waves of sand. You can climb down between the split bastions of the wall until you are in a deep funnel of sand and sandstone open only to the sky. Hound's-tongue grows there, giant horsetails, ploughman's spikenard, and other plants that prefer desiccated and bony places. Foxes bask on the upper ledges of the wall. And from its top, looking inwards, you can see the pool that has accumulated where the drains run backward. It is lonely as any tarn among the fells, and black as a tarn, also, except where fresh dribblings scrabble the surface with red. Moorhens, almost invisible but for their white scuts, paddle across, and gulls nest there and fly upward to the sea. Rushes stagnate in the dead, waveless water.

But on this May afternoon I shall not descend to that Purgatorial landscape, for the spring is swarming round me like a hatching of chickens. Fat little locomotives fuss up and down. The pit-head engines, cheerfully clowning, blow smoke out of their ears. The sky is shrill with larks, and once the ground would have been alive with rabbits. Now, at least for a time, the rabbits have disappeared—though you can still surprise the odd one down in Devil's Hollow—and for consolation we have a richer herbage than ever before. Here, by Brougham Pit, in the days before the mine, the ground sloped seawards in terraces of sand and turf, through which the limestone bulged smooth and lava-like. It is a sampler, now, of bright, tiny, tightly sewn plants: daisy, centaury, tormentil, dog-violet, heart's-ease, lady's bed-straw, and the dry, hairy, field forget-me-not. At midsummer there will be a harvest of wild strawberries, and St John's-wort will add to the red a fancy-stitching of yellow stamens. In summer, too, the burdock will swell up, its huge leaves gathering the dust, its mean thistle-flowers sulking almost out of sight. Then the rosebay will wash over the rubble-tips in an alien, acidulous pink, and beside every cinder path there will be splashes of birds' foot trefoil.

As yet, however, it is not the time for the hot colours of summer. Over towards Iron Green, where the ground has been broken to build the railway embankment, a water-slide of willow ripples

down the slope, and dropped catkins crawl below in a gloom ⅃
will grow, paradoxically, as the sunlight grows. If you creep
through this underwater world of grey-green and yellow-green,
beneath the heave of the leaves, you will find a rocky shore of
boulders and moss and seaweed-like lichens. Here the tway-
blade grows, a sea-green orchid that looks as if it ought to belong
to a mermaid's garden, and the glabrous water forget-me-not, and
primroses. The rubbly floor creaks as you slither among the
polipods and twist under the branches of the willows. Tom-tits
are blown about and blackbirds clatter like burglar alarms. A
maelstrom in the green, a hundred yards away, gives warning of
a shoal of boys, and a drowned dog barks from what seems many
fathoms beneath the waves. You begin to realise why the fore-
men at the mines are called Captains.

('And what with all this water breaking in, they'll be making
them Admirals before long,' says Chunker Wilson.)

Captain Cox is coming towards me now, returning from Mary
Annie Lonsdale, still in his pit-clothes, red as a devil : a small man
with a stride far too long for his legs, who puffs at his self-
importance like a cigar. Years ago, in the Gilbert-and-Sullivan
days of the Amateur Operatic Society, he was a solemn singer of
comic songs, and even today his bass can creak out a greeting at a
distance of a hundred yards, vibrating like the wires of a railway
signal. He pauses when he sees me, and spreads his hands, doing
the honours of the mines as if he owned them.

'Taking a walk?' he asks.

I confirm his deduction.

'I walk miles every day round here,' he says. His gesture
indicates the waste acres : willow, ore, sand.

'Miles every day,' he repeats. 'And all of it underground.'
He turns suddenly, pointing.

'See yonder, by the old quarry.' (The rock cracks down and
whitethorn smokes from chimneys of limestone.)

'I go straight across yonder, first thing in the morning,' says
Captain Cox, 'and I stop for a rest right under that elder-
tree.'

'Under that tree?'

re—hundreds of feet down. Young Brougham-
ed it out for me.'

understandable. The youngest of the Chairman's
n-law.

stooping, mind you, there's no stooping anywhere
in the mine. But there's a bit of a hill, mebbe as steep as the
road over Old Odborough, so that I can do with the rest. And
many a time of a winter morning I think that if there's anybody
up above he'll be starved with the cold, while here am I comfortable as a flea in a midden.'

I say good-bye and he walks away, pausing every now and then
to inspect the cinders as an eighteenth-century landlord would
have inspected the turf. I move off in the direction he showed
me, standing, as it were, on the old man's shoulders. A sickroom
smell hangs over the hawthorns, and by the side of the track a
few cowslips are drooping, their bells smirched with red. Close
beside me is the old lighthouse, on a solid cube of limestone, and,
forgotten away to the left, the derelict windmill older even than
the mines, which became the company offices when the first shaft
was sunk. I make my way between the two of them, down the
slope of the former shore, into Devil's Hollow.

It is a primitive landscape, older by the look of it than anything
but the hill. Yet, in fact, it is not as old as the house I live in.
For Devil's Hollow is a creation of the mines, a wild acreage
enclosed when the New Sea-wall was built fifty years ago. It
lies below sea-level on the one side, below land level on the other—
the forgotten Jordan's Valley of the town. The old swash
channel, dry as a bone, still winds across it, marking the course of
the fifty-years-gone tides. It is sunken, shrunken, shrivelled away
from the world. The huge unbroken curve of the sea-wall shuts
off the sea to the south, and the escarpment of the old foreshore
shuts off the town to the north. Only the spikes and girders of
the pit-heads breaks the skyline. It is the loneliest spot in Cumberland—Scafell Pike is a thoroughfare in comparison. As I
walk down the shingle slope it seems to close round me like a
drawstring bag, the rim of sand and limestone impending above
me, blotting out not only the sight but almost the memory of the

rest of the world. The Hollow sucks me downward like a quicksand. There is an intense vibrating silence. Not even the sound of the sea seems able to surmount the immense barrier of the wall. I sit on a wooden beam, pickled in salt and sunlight, that was once part of a groin or breakwater. The air weighs heavily. The silence tightens round my temples. I feel the blood chugging like an old locomotive along the railroads of my body. Grains of sand, dislodged by my footsteps, go slithering down into little ghylls or crevasses gouged out by flood-rains. The skeleton of a rabbit lies white on the sand. The marrams are stiff as knitting-needles.

Then gradually the pressure begins to relax as I become acclimatised to this strange altitude. The air is breathable again, and though there is not the slightest breeze, the marrams begin to sway as if a local cyclone small enough to be contained in a wash-tub were blowing among them. I bend down to look. The blades are infested with grasshoppers. And now the birds of the Hollow begin to call—birds that seem trapped here forever, unable to fly over the barrier that holds them in : ring-plovers, green-plovers, oyster-catchers, curlews. Larks go up like a flight of balloons at a country fair. Silent meadow pipits impersonate the larks on the ground. A stone-chat bounces up, bright as a pace-egg. A wheat-ear displays its Chaucerian name. Cuckoos announce themselves. Sand-martins play at being bats.

I begin to be aware of the immigrant life of the Hollow. The sand canyon of the old swash channel is marked with footprints that I have not the skill to recognise—hare or rabbit or, maybe, fox; for when the hounds meet here the foxes are sent scurrying among the boulders of the sea-wall or away into the tunnels and wynds of the mines. I follow the line of the channel until the turf begins to grow richer, more tightly stitched with grass. Round rag-mats of dwarf willow lie on the ground, fuzzy with fertilised flowers. There is mud with the sand now, and in places you can see traces of ploughing from the times when turnips or kale were grown, not so much for the value of the crop as to give cover to partridge for the bosses' annual shoot. Soon the dwarf willows give way to sallows, and the turf that has been springy becomes

H

squelchy, and the yellow of dune is replaced by the blue-green of bog.

I step gingerly among the bushes—still sparse and no more than shoulder-high. The young branches are grizzled with lichen and birds flash up like fireworks at every turn. The flowers here are red and dark, as if the haematite were oozing through—ragged robin, lousewort, marsh cinquefoil, and half a dozen different orchids. Farther inwards, where the mud gives place to water, the wild iris spreads a yellow mattress for the flies. This is a sour sump-land, belonging more to the eighteenth century of undrained fens and unenclosed commons than to the countryside of today. The Hollow is inventing its own history, working out its own ecological variations.

I leave the swamp and climb among the brambles and giant horsetails on to the New Sea-wall. It is early evening now, the tide high. The air is salty with the cries of sea-birds. But the Hollow that used to belong twice daily to the sea is oblivious to all this, and shrinks back into itself like the crater of an exhausted volcano.

June

I GO TO my window at seven. It has been raining during the night, and the cauliflower sky lifts and lowers itself as if on the exhalation of trees and chimneys. There is no wind to blow away the cloud, but already the mist is rising and the roofs are steaming like a laundry. On no day of the year does the weather matter more—or not, at least, to me. For this is Whit Monday and the day of the Odborough and Oatrigg cricket match.

It is not, of course, an event to be anticipated with pleasure. League cricket is never gentlemanly, and between near-neighbours it becomes a tournament of malice, envy, and pride. There is no time when the Seven Deadly Sins are more publicly on view— except, of course, for the one obviously unsuited to public view. And when—as here—one of the teams belongs to a small old-fashioned looked-down-upon off-shoot of the main town, then all the resentment of the poor relation is ready to break out like a boil.

The Oatrigg Cricket Club is a team whose existence is as pre-carious as that of the pine marten or the wild cat. Some of the bigger clubs grumble about its inclusion in the league at all, but every now and then the fanatical determination that keeps the club warm suddenly blazes up into the play. A team from a city of 50,000 inhabitants will find itself put out in under an hour for thirty runs, as a bowler emerges who can scythe down the best batsmen in the league, match after match. The next season he will leave the village or turn Saturday-afternoon professional and the club will decline to its hazardous mediocrity, but its right to a place in the league will have been demonstrated beyond doubt.

For Odborough, at least, Oatrigg has always been a team of terror. Even in the great days of the town club when they gave five men to the county side and went unbeaten through the season —even then, Oatrigg could give them a fight. Unbelievable things could happen in the Oatrigg field. I have seen a batsman given out l.b.w. from a leg-glance to the boundary. I have seen a batsman given out caught from a skier that bounced a yard in front of the fielder and was taken waist-high. I have seen a batsman given out for handling the ball when he merely intended to toss it back to the bowler. Older followers of the team remember a wicket-keeper who would deflect the ball into the wicket or knock off the bails with his glove and shout ' Well bowled '. Others will tell of methods of time-wasting to force a draw—of the bowler whose knee-cap always slipped at the right time; of the spectators who would stand in front of the sight-board and have to be moved; of the dog who was certain to chase the ball whenever play needed to be held up. There is no tactical trick which the Odborough spectators do not attribute to Oatrigg. And they do the same to us.

As yet there is not a soul about in the street, for people do not get up early on a Bank Holiday in a working town. The clouds are white, brown edged, in thick, solid lumps like a basketful of mushrooms, but already the sunlight is simmering through from the east. This is the time of day when, according to tradition, Tommy Woods was once seen on the ground with a garden fork and a watering-can. He was a left-arm slow-bowler, and the match was against the top-of-the-league team from Lancashire. Odborough won the toss and were all out for 87 on what should have been the best batting wicket of the season. And then Tommy took 7 for 11.

This is the time of day, indeed, when the field has an existence known scarcely to anyone. The sun is glinting across from what seems the wrong side. The orchard hedge, which is a great banking of shade during cricket hours, is now a banjo of light. Every leaf and raindrop trills and shakes, and out on the turf stray rushes which the mower has missed shine bright as needles. Daisies are opening after three days' grace since Friday evening's cutting. In the longer grass by the boundary lady's smock is out, and the new whitewash on the sight-boards dazzles like an advertisement.

The Cricket Field in Odborough, as in many towns in the North of England, is beside the railway line, since that is the only flat land which is not marshy. A row of wooden palings separates it from the shunting yards, and during the more important matches the engines dawdle up and down and smoke drifts across the pitch and bothers the batsmen. In the days when the L.M.S. ran a team in the Junior League most of their games were smoked out. To the north is the Recreation Hall and the old school of Old Odborough. The benches back against the school wall, off which a six-hit bounces among the skitter of spectators. West is the orchard, bulging above the field. Here along the hedge, under a large overhang of elder and willow, are the old men's seats and the tin shed where the tackle is stored and where once the horse was stabled that pulled the roller. The fourth side of the field opens on to the meadows. This is where the strangers sit, because it is the prettiest side, and they do not know that they will get an ache in the back and a draught in the neck. Here, now, the elder is offering its soup-plates of bloom and the wild rose is twining about the corrugated iron pushed in to block the gaps where the cows break through. The meadow is bright as brass and wicket-deep in grass, buttercup, and dog daisy. Every time a six is hit, the fielder who brings back the ball leaves behind him a little trench that slowly closes as the match goes on. A tidal wave of grass, foaming with seed, is flooding England at this very moment—rolling over the plains and up the valleys, flushing like a bore along railway cuttings, inundating cemeteries, splashing around woods and into orchards, and sending a green squirt even into school yards, building sites, and the County Council Highways storage dump.

The morning moves on. The clouds are trundled reluctantly away and the sun begins to mop up. We can now be sure of a fine afternoon. But what will be the effect of the rain on the pitch? We cannot but wish that it will be bad, for Odborough's hopes this year lie almost entirely on a famous ex-county off-break bowler, engaged at enormous expense and a blizzard of raffles. If the wicket suits him today Oatrigg have had it.

.   .   .

I take my seat good and early under the orchard hedge. The best spots are already filling up, and a gentle fume of tobacco and elder-flower hovers about. Eight or ten players are practising in front of the pavilion. The Oatrigg supporters sit with their backs to the meadow; ladies with their backs to the school wall. Boys sit, for a maximum period of ten seconds, on the railway side, spotting engines with one eye and looking out with the other for a ball to field. Tank Tyson, producing slow donkey-droppers from behind his back as a conjuror produces rabbits, welcomes the chance to get someone to save him the stooping. Old Mr Dale, entering through the gate in striped trousers and with a bone-handled walking stick, parades to the centre of the field, and bows his head over the pitch as in prayer before taking his seat in the orchard corner. Wagtails, thrushes, and blackbirds, that all the climb of the morning had fed their fledglings on cricket-field worms and leather-jackets, are disturbed at their larder. White-throats sing in the hedges, breathless and husky. A bell rings at the pavilion door.

'Buy 'em alive,' shouts the Oatrigg wit. The Odborough crowd does not laugh. The players report at the pavilion. The captains come out and toss. The field is cleared. The wagtails return to the pitch. The umpires emerge.

We are not sure, yet, on our side of the field, who has won the toss, but now Tank Tyson leads out his men. We are not disappointed. With the hot sun after the rain this should be a tea-party for the pro.

The players take their positions, but the Oatrigg batsmen have not yet appeared.

' Playing for a draw already,' says Chunker Wilson at the gate. The batsmen step out of the pavilion, and immediately it is evident that though Oatrigg do not expect to win, they are going to make sure that the Odborough people will have no satisfactions to take home. For Bert Grind is opening the innings, in spite of the fact that it is some years now since he played in the league. His discovery came from an act of protest. For several years he had been a hanger-on at the cricket ground, though, not being a man of enterprise, he did not so much as pick up a ball. But one evening a group of lads playing in a rough corner of the field asked him to umpire, and then suggested he should have a knock. He took the bat, and after ten minutes was still at the wicket. He had hit no ball more than two yards, but he was not out. The lads asked him to declare, but he refused and insisted that they should continue to bowl. They appealed to a group of Oatrigg players who were practising at the nets. Grind clung obstinately to his bat, and as there was none other the game could not go on.

' I'll shift the beggar,' said the first-team fast bowler.

The Oatrigg pitch, being mostly sand, plantain, and shingle, is always erratic, and here, on the outfield, it was as hard as corrugated iron. The bowler fired off a shrapnel of wild balls—short, over-pitched, shooting, lifting, flying—and all of them, except the wides, were patted back with a sound as gentle as the slap of a spoon in a cold Christmas pudding. A fortnight later, Bert Grind opened the innings.

For two seasons he broke more tempers than anyone else in the league. He had not the least desire to score, and when, from time to time, the ball snicked off the corner of the bat to an empty place in the field, it was only with reluctance that he could be persuaded to run. Never did his score reach ten, and once he carried his bat through an innings for eight. Fieldsmen stalked to within four feet of him; bowlers gave up running to the wicket and chucked up dollies or underhands. Spectators swore and slavered into despair, digging cigarette stubs deep into the turf with their boot-heels; umpires got so exasperated that they would give him out l.b.w. if the ball hit him on the backside. After two seasons not even the Oatrigg supporters could stand more of it, and Grind was dropped, but today, for this one match, he is playing again, and everybody in Odborough knows the reason why.

The pro, however, does not. He has bowled three consecutive maidens to Grind and is not displeased with himself. The pitch, he can tell, has rolled out easy after the rain, and with only six on the score-board at the end of the fifth over he feels that Odborough have made a good start.

Thomas Sutcliffe Dale is not displeased either. His eyesight not being too good, what he now sees appears to be a hard struggle between bowler and batsman on a treacherous, turning pitch. And what can be better in cricket than that? He has the greatest contempt for those who wish only to see fours and sixes, remembering with gratitude the old days when there was no time limit on the first innings and a team could bat till six o'clock if it suited them, leaving the other only an hour to knock off the runs. He remembers the time when the one point for a draw could make all the difference to winning the League, and men would sit, in the evening slant-light, their watches in their hands, counting every run and every second. It was these harsh, clenched endings, under a 50,000-watt sun, that were for Mr Dale, the pith of cricket. During fifty years of following the game he had seen little more than an hour of each match, being occupied on Saturday afternoons in the shop, and on Whit Mondays with the Annual Walk of the Wesleyan Sunday School, of which he was Superintendent. So that now, seeing the matches through for the first time, he finds the impatience, the unseriousness, the dissipated interest of the crowd hard to excuse. In his youth the older Methodists had called him ' worldly ' for watching cricket, but he repudiated this with indignation. Cricket was to him as much a part of god-fearing life as *Messiah* and total abstinence. If he had belonged to a sect which believed in saints he would have canonised Verity. His three sons were brought up to cricket as to a vocation, bowling for hours on *The Crown* Green to a single stump till they could drop three balls out of four on a cocoa-tin lid. Two of the boys left the town and joined other leagues. The eldest, apprenticed to the business and no Saturday games for the rest of his life, became a terror of the mid-week Knock-outs. When he took his honeymoon at Morecambe he came home by motor-bike for the Wednesday night to play for his team in the final.

The score is 12 for none. Bert Grind has played five balls of one over and is facing the sixth. It comes over-pitched, not turning, easy and harmless, and he puts out a leg, cautiously as if he were testing the ground for booby-traps, and swaddles the ball in the cotton-wool of his stroke.

' Christ,' says a youth sitting on the grass, ' that beggar doesn't want a bat, he wants a butterfly net.'

Mr Dale straightens himself, looks deliberately about him, and then leans forward and pokes the youth in the back with his walking-stick.

' Look here, my lad,' he says, ' I want to hear none of that sort of language. I've come to enjoy a cricket match and you've brought it down to the level of a common public-house brawl.'

The young man turns round with a what-the-hell-has-it-got-to-do-with-you look on his face, but is unable to find the words.

' Shut up,' says Christopher Crackenthwaite, who is walking along the boundary.

' What the hell has it got to do with you? ' says the youth, finding the words.

' He's seventy; you're twenty. Now shut up or out of the field you go.'

The youth tears up a dock leaf, shoves it in his mouth with a ham-actor's mime of nonchalance, and shuts up.

' Have you heard the Yorkshire score? ' asks Mr Dale of Chunker Wilson.

' Eighty-three for seven. Tattersall's found a patch.'

Mr Dale dibbles his walking-stick into the ground with Christian resignation (they had been 62 for 1 at lunch), rests his chin on the bone handle, and gloomily concentrates on the game.

'What's the Yorkshire score, Chunker?' he is asked again, forty yards farther on.

'A hundred and thirteen for two,' he says, burrowing into a seat as a dog burrows into a rat-hole.

.   .   .

After an hour's play the Oatrigg score is 23 for 1, of which Bert Grind, entirely against his ambitions, has made six. The crowd is beginning to paw and whine and snap. The traditional shouts are raised like responses in church : ' Get a move on '; ' Have a go '; ' Get your bat working '; and then, when Grind had hit the ball perhaps three feet farther than usual : ' Steady, man, steady '. The crowd laughs, having not entirely lost its good humour.

But now comes a more indignant protest. High up on ' The Grandstand ', on the far side of the railway, those who have not paid to come in are demanding their money's worth. Here, on a footpath that runs along the top of the railway embankment and under the churchyard wall, fifty or a hundred men are leaning over the iron railings watching the match. When there are no engines smoking, it is, in fact, as good a place as any. Canon Olds—himself a vice-president of the club and entitled to free admittance to every match except cup-ties—prefers to watch his cricket from here. At one time the club had erected a screen of wood and canvas to block the view, but the wind tore it down in righteous indignation, and, indeed, those of us who sit on the opposite side of the field regretted the loss of the parade of prams and picture-goers which did as much as the sun to show the hour of day and the time-chart of the match. Those with weaker eyes among the grandstand spectators cannot recognise the players with certainty, and if the bowler is fast, they cannot follow the flight of the ball. Nor can they see the scoreboard, though this handicap is overcome by one who records every run in a notebook and counts the balls per over as diligently as an umpire. It is this man now, who loses his patience, tired of marking down maiden after maiden. Vaulting over the railings, he jumps among dog-grass and coltsfoot leaves.

' Like this,' he shouts, ' like this!'—swinging an imaginary bat and swiping six after six.

Bert Grind takes no notice whatever, but his partner, trying to pull the next ball clean into the mouth of the interruption, skies and is caught at the wicket.

A few minutes later the Odborough crowd hums like a beehive, for the second-wicket batsman is a stranger, and the news is buzzed about that he is an all-rounder from the Lancashire League engaged as professional for this and a few more matches. At once he begins to shape to the bowling, but most of the time seems to be tethered to the wrong end. If he scores a single, then Bert Grind bats out the rest of the over. If he scores a four and stays at his own end, then Bert will play through a maiden at the other. He becomes as fretful and frustrated as a dog in a closed car which wants to fight every dog it sees in the street outside. Then, without seeming cause, the Oatrigg captain walks out to the wicket with a bat, which he hands to the new pro, who tests its weight and makes a few practice strokes. The crowd roar with impatience and hurl sarcasms heavy as cobbleducks from all round the field. Chunker Wilson brings out a referee's whistle and blows the captain off-side. The latter goes off, catcalled, hooted, and twitted, bearing the same bat that he had brought in. The new pro faces Tank Tyson, who is bowling slow leg-breaks in the manner of one who takes no responsibility when the ball is out of his possession. The batsman plays gently to mid-off, rushes two yards forward, and then yells in the voice of a town-crier, ' Come on, Bert.'

Bert Grind, clarioned out of a dream, starts, hesitates, and begins to run. Immediately the pro stops, shouts ' No ', and retreats to his own crease. Bert checks himself, looks round, sees mid-off lob the ball to the wicket-keeper, and sets off for the pavilion, in a daze of disappointment. The Odborough crowd, veering like a kite in an alley-draught, applauds him all the way, and Chunker Wilson's whistle blows the whole Oatrigg team off-side.

.   .   .

To be the town's jester is no laughing matter, as Mr Wilson is well aware. He does not ask for a laugh merely for the sake of a laugh. His jokes have a purpose behind them. To a stranger they seem cumbersome and humourless—heavy ironies rolled out as obvious as beer barrels, or understatements farther-fetched than hyperbole. But to the men of Odborough they are part of the moral structure of the town, the whips of conformity. They deal with pretentiousness as a dyker deals with an overgrown hedge, by docking the tops with a bill-hook. They strip off the vanities of class, leaving the uppish to strut along the streets in their patched underwear. They protect the town against the insults of officials and the patronage of petty power. Chunker's jokes are repeated and remembered because they put into words, crude and expressive as the gestures of a clown, just what everyone else is thinking. They are as local as the slate walls. They come from a century of ingrown habit, from generations of communal experience. They voice in one inflection both self-knowledge and self-deception, brag and cringe, pride and the fear of having not enough to be proud of.

Chunker is not really happy among the formalities of a league match. It is, he says, too much like putting on a bowler hat for a game of billiards. His summer pleasure is the mid-week Knock-out competition, which has been a feature of Odborough for generations. Some seasons as many as thirty teams will enter; sometimes no more than ten. Each team may include one listed player from a league first team or two players from a second team. The rest are old players, young lads, shopkeepers who can't turn out on Saturdays, and half a team sheet of long-stops, number-nines, and A. N. Others who have been teased or badgered into having a go. More than one man who has settled himself under the school wall to enjoy a match in the afternoon light has found himself persuaded to make up the number, has slithered on the turf in his studless shoes, dropped sitters, missed run-outs, given away over-throws, and then miraculously snicked the two boundaries that won the game.

Chunker's own team, Wilson's Willows, is less haphazard than this. With Slogger Knox as its listed-man captain and John Dale as its non-listed star bowler, it is almost as well organised as the town team.   Chunker himself does not play, but will sit under the hedge with his referee's whistle blowing shrill protest at every dropped catch, missed run, or l.b.w. decision that goes the wrong way.   Nor is he the only one.   The whole crowd joins in the game, and an experienced spectator can take more wickets than the bowler.   With exhortations swarming round his head like wasps, the batsman will swat angrily with his bat and find himself caught behind the wicket or stumped, and will grumble off, swearing that he didn't know the bowler was going to bowl.   Or a great roar of encouragement will start him running for what he believes will be a cover drive when, in fact, the ball is already in the hands of point.   Or a shout from the boundary will bamboozle an umpire into giving him out when not even the bowler had appealed.   Braces burst at l.b.w.s; cousins walk off the field never to speak to one another again.

The games always have their excitements.   There was the time when Christopher Crackenthwaite, coming in at the beginning of the last over with 19 needed to win, scooped the last three balls on to the railway for a tie.   There was the time when the Working Men's, needing 83, were 72 for 3 and then 79 all out, with four l.b.w. and two run out, and the umpire had to ask for police protection.   There was the time when the final was delayed until the second week in August and ended in such bad light that all the spectators could see was a twilight ballet of inexplicable movements among which, as at the pull of a string, the wickets would suddenly fall.

Wilson's Willows are a practical team, relying on straight bowling and good fielding, given which any team can win in this competition, however bad their batting may be.   But Wilson's is not popular, for the crowd does not admire practicality.   Its favourites are the unpredictables: the men who don't mind making fools of themselves or, better still, the men who mind but go on doing it; the men who enter the field in blue serge trousers and union shirts, and fluke boundaries between their legs, and score more from overthrows than from hits, and drop the easiest of catches, and take the most difficult without knowing how they have done it, and collide with one another in mid-pitch, and raise their caps to the crowd every time they run a single, and lose small change from their pockets and insist on holding up the game while they search for it.   The men who always chuck the ball to the wrong end when there is a chance of a run-out; who are attacked by little dogs in the out-field; who throw away their batting gloves in the middle of their innings and are cracked on the bare thumb the next ball.   Men, in fact, like Tim Tomlinson, who for thirty years kept a milk round and gave it up when motors took the place of horses because, he said, the vibration of the engine would churn the milk into butter.   Or like Watson Hope, who before each ball would nod like royalty to the bowler, granting him permission to start his run, and then be clean bowled if the ball were a straight one.   Or like Christopher Crackenthwaite, who years ago had finished his career with the First Eleven but could still hit a six into the eight-o'clock mail train.

That was cricket worth watching, thinks Chunker Wilson, in a fume of memories and midges, as the ball clanks hard against the tin hut and sends him dodging sideways into a trough of nettles.

.   .   .

The Oatrigg pro is doing well.   Slogger Knox runs up to the wicket, shaking the ball in both hands as if he were shaking a cocktail—(' I didn't know which bloody hand he was going to bowl with,' said the opening bat of one team, bowled first ball.) It would hardly seem that this batsman would mind if he bowled with both hands at once, for his score is 75 and Oatrigg are 120 for 4.   The ground is emptying fast, as people go home for their half-past-four tea, so that fielding has to continue around the legs of men, short-cutting across the boundary.   Small boys are intent on their own private cricket matches, played with a tennis ball and a plank from the railings, and some of the spectators find these more interesting than the main game.

130 for 4.   Tank Tyson resorts to the tactics of despair and puts on Alan Williams, who is one of the best-known batsmen in the league, though as a bowler his one chance depends on his not being known at all.   He bowls out of the wrong hand to begin

with—batting left and bowling right. So that the ball starts awkwardly from the first, and corkscrews high and gawky, like a beginner tennis-player's half-hearted lob, dropping slow and off the wicket. Never was there a ball that was easier to hit : ' like feeding an elephant with a strawberry ', as Chunker Wilson says. But Alan Williams has just one trick up his trouser-leg. He bowls with his foot a yard behind the wicket, so that the un-twigging batsman, seeing the big lollipop of a ball held out before him, bites too soon and is stumped. The pro, however, is not to be codded in this way. The ball floats towards him, gentle as thistledown just outside the leg stump. He steps back and across, waits, and half-pulls, half-bludgeons it, first bounce into the tool shed. The leg-bail accompanies it, first bounce to fine leg. The tea-going crowd, bunched round the gate, cornets with joy. 130 for 5, and twenty minutes later the whole team are out for 142.

Odborough start carefully. First knock is taken by Derek Dale, home from college, as everyone says, ' University ' being an embarrassing word. Old Mr Dale watches, solemn and eager as forty years ago at a prayer-meeting with his extempore prayer ready off-by-heart in his head. Two runs in five overs. Captain Cox sits in his orchard, drilling a peephole from under a tunnel of apple-boughs, and, unlike those on the grandstand who see the players and not the scoreboard, he sees the scoreboard and not the players, except for those on the railway boundary. 1 for 5. The church steeple, which all the first innings turned a shadowed face to the field, now stands in a swirl of sun. 2 for 7 : the pro is out. The field is filling again as folk return from their tea. Spectators on the orchard side sitting under a great weir and overflow of shadow, see midges, high above them, lit by the sun, spinning like coins.

3 for 9. The wicket is turning nasty, making the ball spit and slither. Batsmen jerk and flounder. The diddering light seems half to solidify around them like a yellow jelly, and fieldsmen near the hedge wade up to the hips in a wash of shadow. Councillor Quorum, vice-chairman and team selector, feels his blood pressure increase as if it were being blown up with a bicycle pump. Two more wickets : 5 for 18.

Tank Tyson walks out, and stands, big as a boxer, at the wicket. No need to look round to see where the fielders are placed—they are all within whispering distance.

' You two chaps take care you don't bang your heads together,' he says to silly-mid-off and silly-point.

But he doesn't give them a second look, knowing that from his end mid-off is the angle from which the sun can blind a batsman like thrown acid.

Out on the off-boundary, in the full, black dazzle of the sun, sits Bogey Burrows, his back turned on the game, watching a wren with a mouthful of caterpillars. Twice an over it perches on the heavy roller and then flicks into a tangle of willow sticks piled there after hedge-trimming. When the match is finished, he promises himself, he will search for the nest. There is a groan as from a herd of elephants. Tank has been caught. But only off the knee of his pad. The crowd sucks in its breath like a vacuum cleaner, and Chunker Wilson takes out his whistle but can't find the wind to blow. The batsman relaxes for a moment, then dead-bats ball after ball, while at the other end Derek Dale is watchful and impervious.

The game now settles itself into a long, slow, teeth-aching draw. Tommy Woods, his almost blind eyes running like sores, blubbers out of the field, cursing the team at every step. The crowd is silent, crouched in resentment. Swifts from the gables of the old school skim round and round the field, squealing like whistling-kettles, and sometimes dipping so low that a dazzled slip-fielder will try to make a catch.

After ninety minutes play, the score is 60 for 5. The bowling is slacker now, a draw more obvious, and the crowd becomes both less tense and more dissatisfied. Tank Tyson begins to make more strokes—though with no hope of winning, for there is less than an hour to go. His first boundary brings a noisy, scoffing cheer from the loutish corner; his second brings rebuking applause from the rest. The next ball he is clean bowled.

With six wickets down a draw is much less certain and the more worth the getting. The crowd bends forward, concentrated, hands on knees, pipes going out. It is like the time before a thunder-storm, dark, heavy, dead-still, the very air in a cold sweat. There is no sport on earth which affords the excitement of stone-walling at a time like this. Every ball is a major operation, and at the end of each over the crowd sighs like a patient coming out of an anaesthetic.

Slogger Knox is next in, loitering his way to the wicket with the cunning of twenty years in the league. If anyone can save the match, he can. Once he had been the biggest hitter in the team, but now, in his old age as a cricketer, he has become the prime back-to-the-waller and hope of lost causes. As slowly as possible he takes his guard, hesitating between centre and leg-and-middle, digging his bat hole, looking round the field, and then asking for the sight-screen to be moved. All this is routine tactics—not even the Oatrigg supporters can object, or, at least, not on the Odborough field. Over in the meadow the grass is a burnish of bronze flecked with buttercups. The opening bowler is on again, bowling out of the sun. Slogger seeing nothing but the run-up, makes a demonstration forward defensive stroke in a blood-shot haze of nerves, feels the ball snap at the shoulder of the bat, and hears a yelp of laughter and cheering. The ball, flying over the heads of the slips, has bounced into the boundary by the gate. Still as blind as a slow-worm, he slashes the next ball towards mid-on, and makes the best cover-drive of the afternoon. The applause, now, is of genuine gratitude, for the match is ending not with a whisper but a bang. Moreover, that applause, crackling like a forty-flapper in the dark back-alley of Knox's memory, alerts the Slogger of years ago. It does not matter that at times he can't see the ball, that his breath is short and his joints stiff. He plays his shots out of memory and intuition, swiping at a ball which often is not there, but which, when it is, goes fire-working in one direction or another. Straight drives become boundaries at fine-leg, or are sliced over point, or, sometimes, run true as a master shot. The bowlers wince anxiously around, like farmers trying to catch a bull. Short pitchers on leg-side are pulled on to the railway; long-hops on the off are clouted into the meadow. The fieldsmen disperse and Derek Dale, at the other end, takes easy singles from every ball. In no time the score is

I

100.   Oatrigg are now the time-wasters, but more in bewilderment than in intention—changing bowlers and changing the field. The crowd growl in anger.   The runs keep coming, though with all the fielders well out, it is almost impossible to hit a boundary.   With a quarter of an hour to go twenty runs are needed.   And now Slogger, getting for once a clear sight of the ball, spoons back a catch to the bowler.   Two runs later Derek Dale is out and the rest of the side at 133.

' Match thrown away,' says Councillor Quorum as the crowd departs over the Bridge. ' Ought to be ashamed of themselves.'

The wagtails, the smoke, and the shadows re-annex the field.

July

FIVE HUNDRED feet above sea-level I am, and a fivepenny bus ride above Odborough. July has inundated the land. The rocks surge on the upthrust of the flood : crests of blue, foaming with crystal. Ledges of slate overhang as at the moment of the wave's breaking. Eddies and whirlpools of bracken swish green as brine, and larches squirt water-spouts into the wind. The whole hill heaves under a spume of elderflower, a purple spindrift of vetch. Swamp back-washes down into the troughs between the ridges, shadowed dark with sedge; bedstraw, quartz, and the rumps of wheatears fleck the flood with white. Now is the full tide of the year—trees touching high-leaf mark, grasses splashing two feet above the Plimsole-line in a cream of seed. Flower, bird, and pebble swirl together on the toss of the waves.

Nearly a hundred fathoms below, Odborough lies like a drowned town. The slate roofs shingle the floor of the new sea. The hulk of the slag-bank has foundered among the wreckage of scrap-iron, and the chimneys of the furnaces jut straight up from the sea bottom, trailing seaweeds of smoke. The wharves and breakwaters lie twice a steeple's depth below the tide, useless and preposterous as rusting buckets at the bottom of a beck. All is dead still, in a green submarine light from beneath a glitter of ripples. The faint humming of the furnaces rocks to the surface, and the clanging of the Sunday-evening bells swims upward as from a legend.

.   .   .

Down among the channels of the town, drowned under five decades of months of Sundays, old Mr Postlethwaite hears those bells scarcely louder than I do here. It is a long time since last he went to church, yet no one is a stricter Sabbatarian than he. Nothing could persuade him on a Sunday to buy a match or a cigarette or even an ice-cream cornet for his grandson. Years ago, when he lived behind his chemist's shop, he would turn away any customer who came rattling the back-door on a Sunday, unless it were a matter of urgent illness. Even then, he would refuse to take payment.

'It's a loan,' he'd say. 'I'm doing no business on a Sunday. Come back and pay me tomorrow.'

Then he would return to his fireside and the saved-up copy of Saturday's newspaper and read and snooze while his wife larded their dinner.

Every Sunday evening of summer he puts on his blue suit and his brown trilby, takes his stick with the silver band, and fins up to the church gates among the shoals of worshippers like a lazy old trout among the minnows. The buses, the bustle, the girls on their bicycles, and the queue for ice-lollies outside St Kentigern's Temperance Hotel trouble him not at all. He does not even notice them. He drifts in the deep swim of the evening, where the light seeps down on the shelving roofs and along sea canyons of streets hung with algae and shadows. The doorway of *The Prince of Wales* is a cave from which bubbles of ginny laughter float outwards and upwards. The church bells vibrate in a deep, underwater boom. Mr Postlethwaite, fifty years younger now, with his brand-new cane, salutes Dr Devonshire, goggled like a cod, driving the town's first motor-car over the Railway Bridge.

.   .   .

But what he does not see and what, in another fifty years, he will still not see, is that all round the Market Square the fish-mouths gape and yawn.   For this is the night of boredom—the aimless, workless, dance-less, picture-less None-day of the week. The youths and girls traipse the same few hundred yards of streets —the girls in twos, the youths in sixes and sevens, for without the stir-about of mid-week they cannot even mix together.   Men stand in groups in the Square, not liking to go to pub or club on a Sunday, but ready to wait, hour after hour, on the pavement's edge when fine and, when wet, in a shop doorway.   Without a word said, the same men will meet week after week, at the same spot and same time.   A long, dry, joyless yawn passes from mouth to mouth like an infection.

This is a generation that has forgotten the pleasures of melan-choly, which, for the most part, is a product of solitude.   So now when the Market Square youths are deprived of the mechanical gaiety which they think they desire, there is nothing left for them but boredom.   They have lost that delicious sadness which for centuries has hung over England like an autumn mist; they no longer enjoy those moments when awareness of the shortness of life seems to last so long.

Mr Postlethwaite, whose years have evaporated swiftly as sal volatile, lives longer in these twenty minutes of Sunday than in all the week between.   The top-heavy grass slouches over the graves.

.   .   .

The long evenings of July—so much longer-seeming than the evenings of June because they are already beginning to grow shorter—drift over the town like smoke.   The east–west streets, cupboarded all day in shadow, are now wide open to the light, that fumes the whole length of them, along the line of the bed-room windows.   Old women bring chairs on to the pavement, and communicate one with another along the cable of sunlight as along a telephone wire. People who live ten blocks and two social grades apart on the half-mile of Albert Road, suddenly become neighbours, telescoped together by the sun. Children, dog-tired and dog-dirty, bed down among the pineapple weed of *The Crown* Green, snuggling into the dust. Happy Homes turned British Legion turned Social Club, with its big-bosomed bow-windows, matronly as a Victorian boarding-house, beams across the promenade on to a beach of huts, sheds, broken cars, and old buses turned fowl-houses. The dust heaps little dunes against the railings of the scruffy orchard between the cement yard and the old foundry. It is like the scrag-end of a port on the edge of a dried-up sea.

Just round the corner, however, Furnace Road is in the full flood of the sun. The houses here are like the gentlefolk of the 1860s : *The Furnace Arms* with its portico, once prosperous as it was plump; ' Ironworks Villa ', with its back garden of lilac and poplars running jam up to the cliffs of the slag-bank; and Marsh Edge Cottages, belonging to that Marsh Edge Farm, whose acres lie under the stacks of slag. These, as the early town flourished and decayed around them, did not change face, kept themselves *to* themselves, held bones together with a slapping of cement. For eleven months out of the twelve they stand on their dignity in a mist of smoke from the furnace chimneys and a drizzle from the cooler-reservoirs. Much of the time they can scarcely be distinguished from the slag-bank except when the lights are on. But now they look as if the whole brightness of the sky were being poured through a funnel on to each one of them. They are drenched in light, sopping with liquid sun. Their old freestone window-sills gleam like red currants. There is not a house left standing within a hundred yards to drain off a spoonful of the light or throw a shadow on the ripe paint. They shine out, the blithest buildings on the westward-looking coast from Blackpool to Dunoon. The drinkers in the front parlour of *The Furnace Arms* see their raised glasses brimming with sun.

.   .   .

In the back-yard of one of the few undemolished houses of
Marsh Edge Street sits Mrs Grice.   It is nearly eighty years since
her father brought her to Odborough from Dunner Brig at the
height of the Iron Rush, but she has remained, obstinately, a
country woman.   Her two front windows—one up, one down—
open square on to the slag.   Her back-yard, clamped between
Macnamara's Rag-and-Bone Warehouse and the empty hulk of
the old *Iron Man Hotel*, is sunless almost all the year.   Yet she
has tended it like a stationmaster's garden.   A border of tiles,
along the base of the wall, holds a cubic foot or so of soil out of
which virginia creeper draws acres upon acres of green.   In old
barrels and up-ended chimney-pots are great oil-gushes of ferns—
lady ferns, gathered among the mines; Royal Ferns gathered from
places that few know on the Dunner Mosses; and maiden-hair
spleenworts and hart's-tongues that have come there by themselves.   With her yard door open to the north-west Mrs Grice sits
as in a conservatory.   The creeper hangs a trellis of transparent
hands between her and the sun, and all round her the leafage and
frondage of fern, nasturtium, geranium, and hydrangea spurts in
a luminous spray.   Even the moss on the yard wall glows green
and phosphorescent.   Two years ago a wren had come into Mrs
Grice's yard and begun to build between the spout and the
creeper.   For several days it made scores, or even hundreds, of
journeys an hour, from nest to wall, gathering moss.   It was a
cock's nest and the hen did not lay there, but to Mrs Grice it was
as if the phoenix of childhood had been refledged again.   Sparrows and starlings she has in plenty, gulls from the reservoir, and
from the allotments there stray all the garden thrushes and tits and
finches.   She had seen redwing, without knowing their name, in
the waste land in front of *The Iron Man,* and seen waterhens and
mallard walking down the street towards the slag-bank flashes;
and one winter, on the berberis among the hen-pens, she had
seen an unbelievable bird, like a blown-up chaffinch with a fancy
comb on its wings that an ornithologist would have recognised as
a waxwing.   But none of these had the power that the wren had
had—to pick her up and tuck her into a child's bed of feathers
deep among the gloom and waterfalls of the Drummer Woods.

Mrs Grice is independent. The little that came from her grandfather's small-holding has kept her from the need of claiming the Supplementary, and her daughter comes in every day to clean up and do the shopping. Her house is her own and her back-yard is a landscape she has created. Its walls are of slate— great rough chunks hacked out of the hill of Old Odborough— but the paving is of black tiles crinkled with a pattern of grooves. She knows exactly the course of channels and deltas that the water makes among those crinkles when she swills out the yard; and now, in a miraculous turn of the tide, the sun flows back, up that same course, filling it as molten slag fills the moulds, and drowning and searing Mrs Grice in a burning flood of memory.

.   .   .

There must be thunder about, for the weather in a night has turned sour. The curdled sky slumps down, barely higher than the Ironworks chimney-stacks; a lid has been clamped over the town, shutting off the wind and the view. We stifle beneath it and yet are not even warm, for in the humid air sweat does not evaporate but stays chill and sticky on the skin.

This is the blowsy middle-age of summer—the trees big and unbuttoned, the grass uncombed, scurfy with seed. In the sidings of the railway station between the cricket field and the church, the shunters raise dust-storms of cinders. Willows by the turn-table are grey with age and dirt; elders, no longer flowering, hold out shallow saucers to collect the smuts. Everywhere the fat, coarse flowers that thrive in the dirt are throwing off their heavy outer jackets : hogweed in the rough dog-grass; ragwort, brassy as a slum-landlord; creeping thistle, with a two-day beard of dust. Among broken-down wagons in the scarcely used side-alleys of the sidings, rosebay willow-herb, the off-come, purples the ballast with its chemical stain. Darker purple, among the rummage of long grass, the knapweeds are pushing up—tough little red-heads that will go on staring through half the winter. In the old war-time allotments bindweed strangles the currant bushes, and climbs over fences, its leaves so closely overlapping that they look like the scales of a lizard swambling up the wood.

Colour seems to have been wiped off the earth with a smeary cloth. The once-green of the trees is blotched like the paint on Mrs Grice's back-yard door. The purples and blues and gilts and treacles that glint, at other times, in walls and roofs are now drabbed away and the town looks like a stack of infant-school writing-slates. Only the sky has any life. For beneath the low lid of solid cloud huge lower-flying clouds rumble and manoeuvre. The smoke from the furnaces, damped down by the lid, curls back over the town, falling in a dry, acrid drizzle. An attic in the lower end of Trafalgar Road bursts into flameless fire and lays a horizontal drift of smeach from *The Furnace Arms* to the top of Old Odborough. The eldest Miss Snoot, alone at Mount Pleasant, closes the two-inch opening of the sash-window from which, once, she could never drag her father away. Violet Moss, taking G.C.E. Algebra, sees a smudge of headache across the school windows. John Dodder feels the clamp of the air screwed tighter and tighter. The bowlers in the Jubilee Pleasure Ground —afternoon shift off—seem to be perpetually rolling their woods uphill. Young Timothy Tyson, ignoring the hooter and the fire-engine, makes his fourth circuit of his grandfather's block—top Albert Road along Rotting Road past the shop round by the Liberal Club and back into Albert Road. Off again, now, he starts for the fifth time, making an excitement out of monotony, and watching with immense satisfaction the slow look of puzzlement that comes over the faces of shopkeepers and pavement gossips.

· · ·

The brass of the Royal Temperance Band blows through my window on the lift of the wind. It is the day of the Cricket Club Gala, and round the corner from the Jubilee Road, where the procession had been assembling, comes P.C. Goosefoot, leading the band.

It is a brilliant billowy day—the wind scaring straight from the Irish Sea. All along the side of the road the crowd is planted like an herbaceous border, blooming with colour. The band is passing now, so that I look right down on the top of their hats and the bright blare of their trumpets. First the dancing troups, brought in bus-loads from Furness : little girls of seven or eight in yellowish satin trousers with ear-rings and tambourines; girls of thirteen or fourteen, bosoming out their drummer-boy jackets, or in top-hats and white shorts, blasé as Burlington Bertie. Next, the first decorated car, bearing the Ironworks Queen, and after her, ' Miss Oatrigg ', and the Temperance Band's ' Miss Music ', and the Furness Hospital Gala Queen, and then the champion-chested professional pin-up who has come from Morecambe to crown ' Miss Odborough ' in the Cricket Field. More dancers; children's fancy dress—Dutchmen, Gainsborough ladies, cowboys, bridal couples, postmen, geisha girls, golliwogs, a half-cast negro girl as Miss Althea Gibson, a boy with his head in a gold-fish bowl as a space man, a little girl, naked to the waist, with halves of grapefruit tied to her chest as a hula-hula dancer.

Now come the cycles and tricycles : a girl, in ballet dress, wheeling a huge swan; a boy pedalling inside Donald Campbell's *Blue Bird* (' He saw it on Ullswater!') while his mother walks beside to give a push on the hills. Next, the decorated lorries: *The Crown* Green Garden Party, with a striped umbrella and a trellis of paper roses and all the children of the Green supping tea out of saucers; ' A Day on the Shore,' with ten hundredweight of sand scattered on the lorry-floor, and the children making pies and juggling with pebbles; a bedroom scene from the employees of the Knitting Factory in shortie-nightdresses, with candles and curling-pins and an enamel under-jar well in view; and the girls of Old Odborough New Estate in bathing-suits depicting nothing but themselves. (Daphne Dempster, née Huggins, remembers how she herself had made the same bare-back parade on Coronation Day in a north-west wind that cut like a bacon-slicer clean through the coats of the standers-by.) A pipe-band, girl marchers, trade exhibits—the Furness Laundry Lovelies, Goodness Grocers Cornucopia and ' Why go around half dead when Christopher Crackenthwaite can give you a first-rate funeral ? '

And now ' Miss Odborough ', among a desultory revving of applause that seems to run alongside like a motor-cycle escort. She sits rather awkwardly on her ribboned lorry wearing a velvet cape, and holding a bouquet of roses, wired stiff as a wreath. Last night, at the Gala Dance, she was queen of the quick-step, prettily bending from a neckline two years too low. There among all those who had voted for her and cheered her, she was happy and confident, in a shop-girl's dream that was tangible and sweet as toffee. Everything was normal, everything was what she expected, and her new role fitted her like her brassière. But today she is asked to act an archaic part in a show that was already out of date in her grandmother's time. Her two attendants have been told to curtsey to her when she reached the dais in the cricket field, and she knows they will giggle when they do. She herself is not giggling. She is trying to bow her head to the applause of the crowd as she has been taught, but it is a crowd of children and of the middle-aged. The young men who voted for her are not there now. They do not acknowledge her. They would scarcely recognise her, indeed, garbed as she is for this antique charade. She moves on in her car of state, fulfilling a ritual of fifty years ago, passing between walls more familiar with such scenes than are the eyes who watch her from the pavement.

· · ·

The procession turns out of the Terrace, dragging behind it the ghosts of all the processions which have passed along these streets: Recruiting Parades, Victory Parades, Salute the Soldiers, Holidays at Home, Coronations, Jubilees, Ambulance Parades, May Queens, Rose Queens, Club Walks (the Buffs and the Blues), election campaigns, strikes, and funerals.

The red and purple and yellow, like polyanthus in a back-yard garden, blossom among the grey. So that I am reminded how, at the Coronation, a shiver of blue, as if from the dipping of a score of swallows, flew along the houses at bedroom-window height. And of the parties after the War, when every street had its Queen, and the cars were barricaded out and children ran races, and trestle tables were set up on the pavements, and boys

swilled down dandelion and burdock till they hiccoughed 'Rule
Britannia'.

John Dodder, in Rotting Road, remembers seventeen 'Miss
Odboroughs' or Queens or something or other who have waved
up to his window as this one is doing now. Old Mr Postle-
thwaite, in Trafalgar Road, remembers 'V.R.' in incandescent
gas-mantles outside the Market Hall. Mr Dale, on *Crown*
Green, thinks of Whit Monday Sunday School Anniversary Processions, led by himself and the minister, walking between the
shuttered shops, silk banners waving in the wind—'The Good
Shepherd', 'Suffer Little Children', and 'Remember Thy
Creator in the Days of Thy Youth'. And down in Marsh Edge
Street, Mrs Grice hears the sound of the band as it wheels from
Cumberland Road into Victoria Street, and she goes to her front-
room window and displays the picture of King Edward VII which
she had displayed when the last procession passed along that way
on 26 June, 1902.

My father remembered the occasion well. It was a Thursday,
and the whole day was given up to festivities. At ten o'clock in
the morning the four brass bands of the town assembled outside
the Jubilee Field, together with all the marchers : the Volunteers,
the Cumberland and Westmorland Yeomanry, the Members and
Officials of the Urban District Council, the School Board and
Guardians, the Friendly Societies, the Fire Brigade, the Tradesmen's Association, the Tradesmen and Inhabitants, all of whom
were 'respectfully invited to join'. Except for the very old, not
a man was left indoors, and only women and children were left to
watch. The little town was emptied of its folk that pious morn.
After 'God Save the King', with half of them still singing
'Queen', they began strongly but silently, the bands saving their
breath on the hills—over the Railway Bridge and up to the very
top of Old Odborough. Then down they came, in triumphant
blare and braggadocio, back over the Bridge—the front of the
procession barely missing its tail—encompassing in one great fling
the whole stretch of the town, from Old Odborough Quarry to
Marsh Edge Street and the beginning of the new slag-bank. It
was a walk then, not through a forgotten bottom-end, but through

substantial terraces that still held the glint of the new-cut stone, blue as the bunting that flapped from window and lamp-post.

In the afternoon the children had their turn, being each presented first with a medal and a new penny. Then off on the same three-mile walk—Old Odborough, Albert Road, Victoria Street, *Crown* Green, to Waterloo Road, Westmorland Road, Marsh Edge Street, and back, with no quarter or consideration for shortness of wind or legs. They walked in Sunday Schools, tactfully divided by the bands. In the first batch, St Kentigern's and the Old Church; in the second, the Primitive Methodists, the Wesleyans, and the Bible Christians; in the third, the Baptists, the Salvation Army, and the Welsh Calvinists; and finally, the Catholics, the Spiritualists, and the children unattached to Sunday Schools. After tea the short legs were whipped up again for Children's Sports in the Jubilee Field, and the bands played in the Square, and at five o'clock hundreds of pigeons were let loose to wheel round and round throughout the whole fagged-out evening, until the light dozed off and the fireworks fizzed up above the Jubilee Hill. My father said he counted thirty bonfires.

August

L ow TIDE, and the early sun beginning to dry the flats of the estuary. The level light ducks-and-drakes along the sand-ripples. At the Ironworks, a five-hundred-ton ore boat stands propped against the wharf like a child's toy in a drained-out bath. At such a time it would seem that you could walk across the sands to Lancashire, as indeed, you can if you know how to avoid the quicksands and don't mind getting wet up to the waist. For here the peninsula of industrial Odborough juts right out into the Dunner, half-shutting the river's mouth. Once it lay on that west coast route to Scotland, which involved the crossing both of the Dunner and of the sands of Morecambe Bay. There were guides for the Bay, but over the Dunner the traveller had to find his way by the mark of branches or 'brogs' of broom stuck at intervals into the sand. John Wesley crossed this way before 8 a.m. one day in 1750, hurrying north to save souls in the Cumberland coal-mines. Stage-coaches and diligences made the journey three times per week in each direction between Whitehaven and

Lancaster. Irish cattle, landed at the Cumberland ports, were driven through here to the slaughter-houses of the cotton-towns, My grandmother, coming from Cartmel to join her husband, then in charge of the haulage, crossed the sands by horse and cart. It is said that when she got close enough to get her first clear view of the town she told the carter to turn the horse's head round and go back. Only the tide was coming in and he couldn't.

That was ninety years ago, but the view she saw then was much the same as that which I see today : what there was of the town, and what there now is of it, being hidden by the tubas and trombones of the Ironworks, blaring into the sky. Between them and the shore are now, as then, only shacks, railway lines, and half-marshy fields running west towards the mines. The Iron-works Pier is as busy as ever it was, for because of the rise in freight charges on the railways, it has paid to open the harbour again, and on the high tides of each month half a dozen small cargo boats bring in ore and carry away pig-iron. They are loading one now to sail in the afternoon—the locomotive shunting the trucks, and a mechanical grab spearing, swallowing, and dis-gorging like a cormorant.

But the old Ore Pier of the mines was abandoned long ago. It is separated from the Ironworks Pier by a channel that admits the tide into a small creek where sea-lavender grows beside the ruins of the burnt-down fever hospital. So that it stands like an island in the sand, half-way between the Odborough Market Clock and the Lancashire shore of the estuary. This is where they used to build ships, fifty or sixty years ago—small coasting vessels of about three hundred tons : the *Happy Harry*, the *Iron Duke*, and the *Mary Annie Lonsdale*.

Tommy Woods, the left-hand slow bowler who once bowled out Furness for eleven, served his apprenticeship here—as much to cricket as to ship-building, for there is a splendid practice pitch just beside the old railway. The lines were taken up long ago, but the indentations of the sleepers are still marked in wild thyme, and the track makes a thoroughfare through the ragwort and sea-holly. You can see here the ramp from where they launched the boats into the creek—a steep mound of ore-rubble, once red as brick, but now greened with horse-tail and yellowed with toad-flax. The concrete floors of the harbour-master's office and the marine stores kept by Christopher Crackenthwaite's grandfather stand out bare among the turf like ancient pavements revealed in an archaeological dig. In the histories of the twenty-second and twenty-third century this spot will surely look very much the same as all the other ruins in the hills round about—the Roman Camps, the Bronze Age barrows, the flint factories, and the stone circles.

During the great Iron Rush, however, in the last years of the last century, the Pier was the promenade of the Odborough people. No one in those days lived far from his work if he could help it, for that only meant having farther to walk, and most of the men were proud of their town and did not want to get away from it. Even the bosses built their big houses close to the furnaces, where they now stand on islands of black privet among the railway lines and scrap-iron. The new houses around the hill of Old Odborough were unbuilt then, and the streets behind the slag-bank—now derelict and deserted—were packed and pullulating with children, so that instead of toiling farther by train or wagonette, it was easier for the mother to slip past the furnaces and over the railway on to the Pier and the iron shore beside it. Nor, indeed, would the toil have brought them anything better. For except when the wind is in the north-east, here is air as pure as any in the county; and here are sands as flat as a football field, where children may wade out almost beyond call and yet be no more than knee-deep in the water.

Whole families came here, carrying clothes-swills of food—scones, ham-sandwiches, and cold Cornish pasties. Isaac Cross-thwaite would be there with his ice-cream barrow, and the fish-women of the harbour cottages would light the fire under the copper and boil jugful upon jugful of water for brewing tea. At the time of the launching of the *Happy Harry* and other boats there would be brass bands and a marquee and a parade of hard hats and parasols. Old Crackenthwaite made more out of selling dandelion and burdock than out of the joinery and plastering business he had just bought for Marmaduke, his son.

Then there was the Regatta, which survived, on and off, until
the early 1920s, so that I can remember being taken to it by my
grandmother when I was only six or seven. We had to walk, of
course—the full mile of Furnace Road, and then nearly half a
mile across the heath to a viewpoint on the shore. But walking
was no discouragement to a boy whose uncles had walked twice
that distance to school and who had never seen any form of public
transport but the train. What mattered to me was that this
patch of seaside was getting its due, was being treated rightly and
properly as if it *were* the seaside. For in a dim, confused way I
realised that this was not usually the case. The Pier, somehow,
had not quite the same prestige as, say, Southport. Now, at last,
the Pier had its crowd, its boats, its ice-cream carts, its stewards
with rosettes in their button-holes. There were printed programmes and a blackboard with numbers and a man who shouted
through a trumpet. Yet what it was all about I had little knowledge of.

The boats sailed close to the shore, so that through the white
and red sails you could catch glimpses of the hills or of the derricks
of Furness Shipyard. But that they were racing it was impossible to believe—they moved so slowly; they were so quiet; they
took so little notice the one of the other. And in any case, I
myself took little notice of them, or even of the sea, for like not a
few children born beside it, I had not the slightest wish to be in it
or on it. The sea always looked dirty to me, and I was by nature
as well as by training an exceptionally clean child. There were
times when I could be persuaded to follow aunts and friends three
inches deep into the tide, letting the water slosh over my ankles,
but I loved far more to run barefoot on the turf behind the shore.
This, indeed, was why I so much valued the Pier, being as I called
it, a 'grassy' seaside. Here there was next to no shingle, which
was a torture to a bare foot, nor was there much of marram, with
its malicious skewers. At least what there was of either of these
toe-traps, or of broken glass, broken shells, sea-holly, and cinders,
was confined to a ten-yard belt on the withering rim of the sand.
Behind was a mattress of thyme and tormentil, milkwort and
Dutch clover, on which the foot bounced as on india-rubber. It

K

smelled, I suppose, like a pot pourri, but I doubt if I ever noticed this. Sense of smell played little part in the joys of my childhood as it has played little part for me since. It was the feel of the ground that delighted me—the sponginess of the herb on the ball of the foot, the tickle of grass between the toes, the dint and impression made by the heather which grew, not bush-high, but flat on the surface, like an embossed pattern on a wallpaper. Once, on a holiday in Scotland, I had seen the poorer children running unshod about the streets; I had watched a little girl, delivering milk, walk barefoot along a carriage-drive of cinders, testing every clinker as cautiously as a fakir walking on live coals. It had seemed to me then to be a most delectable act of courage and freedom. For I was not brought up in a home where a child was allowed liberties of that sort, and it was only at the seaside that I could set foot on the soil that had bred me. I took the chance with rapture, and ran, savage as a rabbit, among the rest-harrow and sheep-droppings, which did not disgust me, though they stuck to my feet like little bunions. The ships leaned, tacked, and dipped like slow-motion terns; the tide toppled over its tip; and, strap-hanging to my grandmother, I clopped the mile and a half back home in boots now two sizes too small.

They had told me when I was in Scotland that the bakers there kneaded the dough with their feet, and from that day to this I have not known whether to believe them or not.

.   .   .

The morning circles on. The sand-banks in the estuary are now dry and yellow as sawdust, but the channels are broadening in a blur of sea-pies and sun, and the opposite shore is merely a shade behind a dazzle. It is easy to see why the shore is now as deserted as in Wesley's day. The Ironworks stand with their swords of flame guarding an Eden to which, in fact, no one wants to return. When the wind is in the north-east the smoke of that flame spreads a screen between the town and the Pier from which the visitor turns back without curiosity. A quadruple line of railway, running from the furnaces to the mines, keeps out cars as a grid keeps out cattle. Industry, indeed, protects the shore more thoroughly than the National Trust could ever have done.

There is about a mile of it, cut off from sight of the open sea by the rocks of Odborough Point and from sight of the fells by the old pier. The shore-line hardly ever feels the whips of a wave, so that there is no perceptible difference between the slope of the shingle and the slope of the sand, which is dark and rather muddy and cracks like a pie-crust when you step on it. The shingle, for its part, is pale and mauve, an uncemented conglomerate of blue slate, pink granite, red sandstone, and the brick which will soon be the commonest pebble on the beach. Above the shingle is drier sand, with sea-holly, its leaves like those of ordinary holly dipped in Epsom salt for Christmas decoration. Higher still the sand is tucked and crinkled into a miniature dune-land—hills no higher than a child, chines and scoopings and sand-slides, becks and drains running red with the seepage of the mines. It is small, shut in, and seemingly contrived : a rockless rock-garden or a golf-less golf-course.

Further inland, about a hundred yards from the shore, the railways begin to spool out their tangle of parallels, and there are cinders mixed into the sand, and knuckles of ore rolled under brambles like lost cricket balls. Wagons stand abandoned beside broken-down buffers or toppled over at sand-choked points, and the stonechats perch upon them as if the red of their breasts were intended by nature for camouflage among rust.

This is the place where, as a boy of eight or twelve, I walked every Sunday morning with my father and my uncle, coming down Aaron's Lonning and past Limestone Hill. Here in bowler-hatted respectability, solemn as sidesmen, they inspected this landscape which had grown, flourished, collapsed, and decayed in the course of their life-time. They walked steadily but unhurried, scraping up little sandstorms of red dust with the ferrules of their walking-sticks, while I ran in front with my little silver-headed cane, the dog scuffling beside me. Once, a few years later, in the end-of-term dog-days, after matriculation, half a dozen of us slipped out of school, walked down to Odborough

Point, and watched a man catching eels and cutting the swallowed
hook out of an arm-length of writhing guts.   Soon after this we
began to take our first girls in that direction, or wandered, without girls, half-hoping we would catch them changing among the
rocks.   But, already, our trips were self-conscious, almost apolo-
getic; already we were beginning to look elsewhere.

For this frayed edge of the Iron Age, the mines, the pier, the
wagon-cumbered shore, belonged to the world of the twenties, the
depression, and the dole.   This was the hole that somehow we
were going to climb out of.   The bedraggled, red landscape sub-
sided into the limbo of memory.

So that visited now it seems like a stage set after a performance,
with the footlights off and the house lights on and brooms and
mackintoshes lying across the painted balustrade.   Close your
eyes, and it all comes right again.   The new railings, the tractor,
and the ploughed-up acres behind the old Harbour House vanish,
and soil and turf shine out red and green as clear gums.

The few children who still come to the shore walk dazedly, as if
moving through someone else's dream : wizened little mothers of
twelve and a half dragging families far larger, it would seem, than
families still can be; pre-Crockett boys carrying forked sticks to
prise off the mussels that were condemned thirty years ago as
unfit to eat; babies with lollipop-plugged mouths wallowing in
prams that reek of the incontinence of three generations.   These
are the children of parents who have rejected the mirage of the
new prosperity and wear poverty as blithely as a tramp wears a
dog-daisy in his button-hole.   They have been brought up in
houses barricaded against the Health Visitor, the Education
Officer, and the man from the Labour Exchange—houses where
the windows are blocked up with cardboard boxes from the dust-
bins of grocery stores, and the lobbies are hung with old clothes
from rummage sales.   They are as healthy as rats and roll on
rag-mats sucking at a verminous independence.   These, in their
yelping and not-yet-resentful ignorance, see the shore as their
great-grandparents saw it because they have never had the chance
to see anything else.   These can sneak past the swords of flame
and wriggle back into the Iron Paradise.   They paddle in the red

drains, find unbroken bottles and break them, and collect leather belts washed up from presumed drowned bodies, while the sun leaps at them and licks their chins like a puppy.

.   .   .

The tide is thrusting hard, now, gurgling up the bottleneck of the channel. This is Odborough Point—the most southern tip of the town, of the parish, and of the county. Here the limestone claws at the sea as it did before the town was even thought of. Only the wind and water make a mark here, and that so slowly that not even the earliest man to have discovered this shore could find much altered in the two, three, or how many it was, thousand years. Here we are quite out of sight of the town, huddled round by the cliffs. The mines are not more than a hundred and fifty yards away, but we would know nothing of them here, except that sometimes, on a rising tide, the surf suds red with the wash of a drain. The mines are not only behind us, they are beneath us, underneath the sea, so that if Captain Cox deserved to be an admiral, as Chunker Wilson said, he deserved, also, to be a submarine commander.

The rocks paw at the water, and between each claw of the pad there is a cleft or fissure or cove, where you can lie private as a hermit in a grotto. The sea-spleenwort grows in exactly the same crack as that where it was recorded sixty years ago in the *County Flora,* and the ploughman's spikenard grows not very far away, though that is not recorded in the *Flora* at all. It is common enough, of course, in North Lancashire, where my grandfather came from, and I believe it must have followed him across the sands, feeling itself to be at home wherever a Nicholson was settled. So that it was only right that another Nicholson fifty years after should find it and claim it for Cumberland. The foot of the cliff splays out like the talons of an eagle clutching a globe at the base of a Chippendale table-leg, and the talons are dug deep into bladderwrack, baked dry as a crust on top, but, below, a simmering moisture of crabs and whelks and mussel-shells. Already the barnacles, scattered over the rocks like little cement-mixers, are preparing to open their shutters to the tide. The water begins to slop over the lower ledges, squirting itself into crannies and then siphoning out again with a sucking sound, as of a tongue clucking in a hollow tooth. The larger boulders of the shore now stand as an archipelago, with a valance of seaweed heaving round them at the push of the tide. Because of which we cannot return by the shore, but have to climb up the cliff-side by one of the slanting chimneys of turf and thrift and brambly over-hang, till we reach the top of the Point. Here, beside the old wind-mill where George Threlkeld set up his first office over a hundred years ago, we are stepping on the corn of the big toe of Cumberland. Fifty-six feet above what was sea-level two hours ago, we look up to the eighty-feet of Limestone Hill, half a mile away, and the ninety feet of St Kentigern's Hill, a mile and a half away, and to the hundred feet of Old Odborough behind that, and still farther behind, to Black Fell and all the rest. If there were a man with a telescope on Scafell Pike, the highest point in England, he would see us and would no doubt wave to us as fellow mountaineers.

.   .   .

But if we were to wave back it might cause a misunderstanding, for Violet Moss and her sister have come for an afternoon bathe in the little bay that lies between the Point and the end of the sea-wall. It is a favourite place of these girls. Few people come there now, and the children born in the new housing estates of Old Odborough have scarcely even heard of it. Yet fifty years ago when Grandfather Moss was a wood-boss at the mines, it was the proudest spot in Odborough, throwing out an arm to hold back the sea from the workings. Even today, when there is scarcely anything for the sea to be held back from, it still keeps a dingy dignity. And though surrounded by the mines and, indeed, made by them and out of them—for the limestone of the Wall came from the Company Quarries—it is one of the cleanest stretches on the north-west coast. There are no rotting wharves or break-waters or broken-down boats as there are round the old pier. Nor is there the slime and smear of oil that we find on the open coast. Instead the little V-necked bay is neat and secluded as a private swimming-pool.

That is why Violet Moss likes it.   Her sister would rather go to the Oatrigg end of the Wall, where there will be more people to watch a figure that is, in fact, worth watching.   But for Violet it is the snugness of the bay that makes it dear to her; its old-fashioned look; its homeliness : like that of her grandmother's kitchen.   She climbs up among the boulders till she is hidden from the world in a cubicle with walls of limestone.   Here she undresses and lies on the hot stone with her swim-suit only half pulled on.   Her sister flurries among the kittenish waves, keeping an eye on the dip of the path.   But Violet lies in an euthanasia of sun, letting consciousness evaporate and the stupor of the heat overcome her.   This is the last week before the School Certificate results, and she will neither think, nor foresee, nor wonder.   She feels her body levitated under the fume of the heat.   She feels the whole wall tremble and surge.   The long curve of limestone swells like a soap bubble inside which floats the town, evanescent as a shadow.   Violet hears voices and pulls up her swim-suit.   Two lads from school have arrived on bikes and persuade her sister to let them show her the tunnel among the boulders that Violet knows for certain she has been shown twice this summer already.

Violet lies still and the bubble goes on swelling.   Everything that she knows is reflected in the bubble—the mine, the town, her home, her family, her life up to this moment, and the lives of her parents before her.   And all of it is heart-tearingly dear to her, for reasons she does not understand, for reasons that in a few years' time will make her turn her back on the town, and for reasons that, years later, will make her turn to it again.   The sud of summer floats, hangs, expands in the air.

She stands up, peeps round the corner of her cubicle to make sure that the boys are not coming back, and begins to put on her clothes as quickly as she can.

.   .   .

It is not so much that the tide goes out as that the sands come in. For half an hour or more after the time of high tide the water seemed to be hesitating, slipping back and then edging up again, and the whole Oatrigg shore, from the wall to the dunes, was whinnying with ripples and gulls and children. Now, the sand has heaved itself up like a man waking from sleep, and the tide runs back off its ribs and shoulders. The children are left paddling in foot-sized quicksands of their own making; the beach-combing birds hurry back to business.

Immediately the water-traffic, which had been silent under the flat-iron of the tide, begins again. Little stranded pools wriggle to get back to the sea. Runnels nose this way and that along a Hampton Court Maze of ribbings. And from between the boulders of the wall unsuspected becks and backwashes appear, each with its own four-inch-deep channels that not even the stormiest sea can obliterate for long. At the same time the tide of man flows inward, towards the land. The children settle down to sand-castles or run back to family picnics in the dunes. Young girls—shy as a fig-leaved Eve about their own bodies—unself-consciously strip and dry their younger sisters in full view of their boy-friends. Mothers gather up baskets and spades and begin to worry about buses. A few young men, out early from the Works, run down the sands to catch the tail-end of the tide, but for the most part the beach is empty.

For Oatrigg, at any rate, the shore is shut up for the night, and only visitors stay on after tea-time. The Oatrigg children clatter sulkily up the Main Street, with the air of having had enough of the beach. The women bring chairs and knitting on to the pavement. The men stand around the *Harbour Arms* or sit on seats by the bus-shelter, their backs turned solidly to the sea.

This is the time when the year looks dead and done for. Green-ness has gone out of the world and fruitfulness has not yet come. Everywhere there is a dry, mean-looking seediness. The grass is brown as leather, and down by the Oatrigg Pool the pink rest-harrow is in pod, the yellow hawk-weeds are fluffy with seed, and the once-blue sea-holly is merely a pin-cushion of empty grey calyces. Even in the allotments the flowers look tattered and neglected—heavy marigolds, fat over-blown roses, and sweet-peas like birds exhausted after a long migration.

.   .   .

The sun ebbs with the tide, and now, in the slant of the light, the dimples of the land emerge from their day-time flatness as the ribs of the sand emerge from the sea. The dunes become a mountain vista of ridges and escarpments, sun-scoops and peaks. Seen one way, the marrams are a forest of straw cypresses on fire in the sun; seen the other way, they are a striping of blurs against the dazzle. Each stalk makes the angle of a pair of compasses with its own shadow. In the glitter of the sunset the wet beach is like a sky, while the sky, drifted with a mottle of cloud, is like a shingle beach. The sun submerges, couples begin to saunter out from the village : girls with backs and shoulders still bare, dusking themselves in the heat that seems independent of the sun. They wade through the shadows as through a lake.

On the other side of the dunes the orange-and-purple estuary lies emptied of children and water. On the edge of the out-of-sight sea, black-backed gulls bark and skirmish. One or two men, dark as blackberries, are digging for bait.

The girls in the dips of the dunes shiver but do not move to cover themselves. In the village the lights go on in the pub and the chip-shop. Dogs are being whistled home from sniffings and scufflings among dropped picnic wrappings in the front street and dusty mallows and groundsel at the back. The green dusk hangs over the landscape like a huge moon. The sea-wall, with no sea now to bother about, dams up a great reservoir of shadow in the Devil's Hollow. The tip at the Ironworks' slag-bank finds—for the first time this day—enough dark to make itself visible, and throws up its own small sunset, which will grow brighter as the other one fades. The sailors from the boat which has come in on the afternoon's tide make their way—not very hopefully—up Furnace Road, seeking a night's pleasure. A giggle of thirteen-year-old schoolgirls hovers round and pursues them like a swarm of midges.   The Ironworks' buzzer announces ten o'clock.   The salmon fishers go out and set their nets in the channel; the first lights on the Lancashire shore poke long splinters across the sands, from county to county.   And, far out in the estuary, the tide is already on the turn.

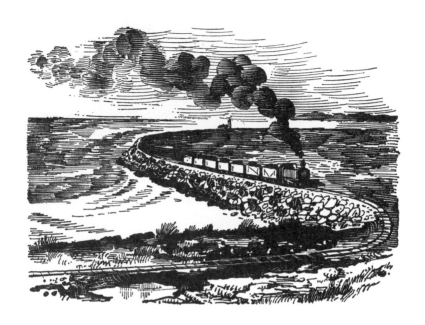

September

'BECAUSE,' SAID Chunker Wilson, 'why the hell should the town grow up all skew-whiff, like a dog's hind leg, and that a broken one, if it weren't for Aaron Tyson?'

'Never Aaron Tyson,' said Watson Hope.

'Him or someone,' said Chunker. 'It stands to reason.'

He, himself, and half a dozen others were standing, though not to reason, beside his billiard-table drinking herb-beer—all except P.C. Goosefoot, who, being on duty, was sitting down. It was that time of the year when the darkness, after having ebbed for three months nearly out of memory, begins to wash back again in the evenings. There was a gentle ripple of shadow along the channels of the streets, and all the girls and young soldiers were splashing in it, excited as wading-birds at the return of the tide.

'See here,' said Chunker.

He took a piece of chalk and drew a parallelogram on the top of his counter, leaving one side open :

'Now A is Old Odborough,' he said. 'B is the Pier, C is Odborough Point, and D is Oatrigg.'

He added a few wavy lines to the left, bottom, and right of the figure.

'That's the sea,' he said.

Watson Hope took his pipe out of his mouth.

'At high tide,' Chunker added quickly.

'Now,' he said, 'they found the ore at C and they had to take it to A because that's where the station was going to be. And what did they do? They laid a laal rickety line all along the Mains to the Pier, and then up the edge of the marsh past where the Ironworks is now. So that when they opened the new shaft at Oatrigg they had to run another line along the sea-wall '—he drew a bow-window shape on the left of his plan. 'And then take every blessed wagon-load on a Cook's Tour of South Cumberland, from D to C and C to B and B to A.'

'Knows his alphabet backwards,' said the constable.

'And for why?' asked Chunker Wilson.

'And for why not?'

'I'll tell you for why not. Because anyone with the sense to dig a pipe-track let alone sink a shaft knows that the shortest distance is what the crow does, which is from C to A.'

'Right through Aaron Tyson's farm.'

'And what would have happened if they'd laid that line from C to A?'

'Old Aaron would have milked his cows in the signal box.'

'You'd have the Ironworks opening up where they should have been, half-way between the mines and the station, instead of stuck on the bottom corner, like a seg on a boot. And all those rotten old marshy fields around Rotting Pool would have been covered with the slag-banks and foundry and shunting yards. So that when it came to building the houses there'd have been no room this side of the station and they'd have had to build up the hill of Old Odborough. So that instead of being born and bred as we were on a hundred acre of sump and sedges hardly fit to rear geese on, we'd have all spent our childhood on the delectable slopes of Mount Pleasant, filling our lungs with God's fresh air.'

'So that?' said P.C. Goosefoot.

'So that Watson, here, instead of growing up a weedy reed with a bad stomach, wasting his time playing billiards and supping glass after glass of this here nettle and dandelion muck, would be a fine strapping specimen, climbing Black Fell before breakfast, and swilling good ale every night in *The Prince of Wales*.'

'If it hadn't been for Aaron Tyson, like,' said Watson Hope.

'If it hadn't been for Aaron Tyson. And there wouldn't have been no need for Furnace Road, neither, and old Richard Nicholson would never have laid it.'

'That would be the grandfather of him that writes books,' said Watson.

'It would. And he'd have written no books neither if it hadn't been for that road.'

'Damn silly books they are, an all,' said P.C. Goosefoot. 'There was one with a policeman in it—— '

'We lived next door to the Nicholsons when I was a lad. Fourteen boys there were in that family, and never a girl among them. And the father was a foreman at the backside of the Ironworks then, but before that they said he was in charge of all the horses and the carting, for he'd been a farmer at Cartmel before he came to Odborough. So it was him that carted all the chippings from Castle Quarry to make that road. They didn't go in for civil engineering in those days—they just dug a track and tipped in a ton of gravel and ironed it flat with a steamroller. Well that road was straight as a die and near a mile and a half long, the station being where it was and the Ironworks being where they had to be on account of Aaron. So that it was the only road in Odborough that looked as if it was going anywhere, notwithstanding it went nobbut to the old pier and if you wanted to go any farther you had to swim.'

'At high tide,' said Watson Hope, with the air of a batsman who had waited a long time for that particular ball.

'Well, Richard Nicholson laid the road, and the Works pony and trap would meet the directors at the station and bowl them along to the furnaces, for a ten-minute inspection of the plant once every three months and a cracking great dinner afterwards. But that was scarcely enough, you'll admit, to justify a beautiful road like that, with getting on for fifty brand new lamp-posts and not a single house the whole length of it. So they built the Market Hall at the top end of it, with a clock so that every man walking home along that road could see if he was late for tea. And then they built *The Prince of Wales*, to make sure he *was* late. And then they built the Library with Carnegie's money, and the Banks with our money, and when they wanted education they turned the Library into an Evening Class Institute and then turned that into a Secondary School. Which is where Richard Nicholson's grandson went, twenty-five years after the old man was dead and gone, to learn French and Latin and Algebra and all them other things that poor ignorant beggars like Watson and me know nowt about.'

'Which is why he writes the books?'

'Yes, because all the time year by year, they'd been adding rooms and huts, patching here, patching there, till the whole place was packed and dark and airless as a hen-house. While all the time the damp was rising out of the old Rotting Pool Marshes, and the furnaces were belching like volcanoes. So what could a lad do but get a weak chest and end up good for nowt but mebbe write a book now and then.'

'All the same,' said P.C. Goosefoot, 'There was no call to bring in that bit about the police.'

'All the same,' repeated Watson Hope, 'It was Aaron Tyson who was to blame. You see, it'll come to that in the end.'

'But, man, it was Aaron,' said Chunker, a bit exasperated. 'Look here, can't you remember the man?'

'Just in so. He'll have been dead nearly fifty year. He used to deliver the milk at the Mines Office when I was a lad apprenticed to the stores. He'd walk all the way from Limestone Hill, every morning, with his half-gallon in a can, and he never said a word to nobody. And half the time he was in next-door-to-rags. They said that when he died he owned nobbut what he stood up in. Except for his farm.'

'Except for his farm,' said Chunker Wilson. 'Now when Aaron was a young man he had no thought for farming. His father rented those forty acres from His Lordship, but not one farthing would he pay out in wages, least of all to his own son, so Aaron would go and get a job up in the Lakes at one of the slate quarries. That was where he met George Threlkeld. Threlkeld was running the quarry and also one of these lead- or copper-mines you find among the fells. Now the old man Tyson was taken badly and they sent for Aaron, and he came home for a week. And while he was there he took a walk down the Mains towards Odborough Point. I can hear my father telling this as though it was yesterday. It was a September day and he was gathering a capful of blackberries.'

He paused for a moment, and he and Watson saw, like a magic-lantern slide thrown on the wall, the scene as it must have been in the days before the mining—the rock barely breaking the surface, the shelves and terraces of turf, the blackberries bucketing down the white stone, and the sheep feeding over what are now the cavities and man-traps of No. 4 Shaft and Mary Annie Lonsdale.

'It was then that Aaron noticed the ruddle,' went on Chunker. 'Oozing red out of a laal syke, it was, just as if there were a running sore in the rock. And he thought to himself: Mebbe there'll be iron ore yonder. And when he went back to his work he mentioned it to George Threlkeld, and before Martinmas the prospectors had been and looked and found the ore and a company had been formed to dig the first shaft just beside the old wind-mill. Aaron's father had died by now and he was back again at Limestone Hill, and one day George Threlkeld went to see him and offered him the job of foreman when the new shaft was opened. Aaron said nowt at first. Then he asked for a day to consider it. Now Aaron's father had saved a laal bit of money. God knows how he'd done it—but that family had lived on taties and weak tea for generations and never spent a ha'penny if it wouldn't bring them a penny back. So there it was, in two or three old tin boxes, shoved to the back of a cupboard—mostly in sovereigns mixed up with old medals and George IV pennies and his Total Abstinence badge and such like. And Aaron wrapped it in his muffler and set off to Whitehaven that very morning. That was before the railway came to Odborough, and he walked the thirty-three miles to His Lordship's office and went in and said he wanted to buy his father's farm. Well, it was only a scatty laal lump, half marsh, half heather and bent, and whether it was because the mines were likely to put paid to farming, or whether he talked the agent round, I don't know. However——'

Chunker stopped. Watson Hope nodded as, years before, in the mid-week knock-outs, he used to nod to the bowler before every ball.

' He bought that farm. And the next day he went round to see George Threlkeld, and told him he'd got a proposition to make. He said he'd come in not as a foreman but as a partner. He said he was a landowner now, and if they wanted to start mining on his land, as they would if that first shaft paid its way, then they'd got to take him into the firm. Them, he said, were his terms. Then George Threlkeld told him——'

He waited but no one spoke.

' Told him that though his farm was called Limestone Hill, and thought it was not more than half a mile from the Point, it was well outside the limestone belt. There was about as much chance of finding ore on it, he told him, as of opening treacle-mines up Dunnerdale. Then he offered him the foreman's job again. " Thank you, no ", said Aaron. " My land may be no use to you, but it served my father and it'll serve me. And Good Day to you, George," said Aaron.'

' You're right there,' said Watson. ' I've heard him many a

time when he brought the milk. Old Mr Threlkeld would be strutting about the office like Lord Heap of Muck, and his son there that married the Brougham woman, and Aaron would slop up and down with his breeches arse very near out, and he'd nod to old Threlkeld and say " Good day to you, George," just like that. And once the son says to him : " That's no way to speak to my father," and he give him a great long look like as if he were a truss of runner beans with the blight. Then he says again: " Good day to you, George," and the old man says : " Good day, Aaron," and Aaron looks at the son and says to him in a kind of pitying, humouring way : " You're nobbut a lad." And he picks up his can and out he goes.'

' " Good day, George," ' said Chunker. ' Every man at the mines used to say it behind his back, but no one but Aaron Tyson would say it to his face. And that was the one recompense he got for planting the pip that grew into this here beautiful bloody town—the right to call Captain Brougham-Threlkeld's father by the name of George. Because he couldn't run a farm, none of that family ever could. Ditches choked with fool's celery and hedges bolting away into copses big enough to shelter ten thousand spadgers, but not one bit of use to keep a bullock in a field. He had next to no stock—a few cows, mebbe, but he made more out of compensation for those that got knocked down by the pit engines than that he did out of the milk.

' If he made any money at all,' said Watson Hope, ' it was out of the pigs and hens that he fed on the swill he collected every day from the offices and bait-sheds. If you threw away the core of an apple he'd bend down and pick it up and take it back with him to the pigs.'

' But that was when he was an old man,' said Chunker. ' The time I'm talking about was just after he bought Limestone Hill. That was the time before they opened the railway. So that every hundredweight of ore and all the timber for the pit props had to be carried by horse and cart—except for what was floated across the estuary to Furness in flat-bottomed boats at high tide. Now the easiest way from the Point to Old Odborough was by the lonning that runs right through the farmyard of Limestone Hill,

L

and the carters would have many a crack with Aaron as they passed through—not that he ever had owt to say, but he never objected, like. Then came the news of the railway, and George Threlkeld gave orders to lay a light line that would take the bogies from the mines to the station, and that line would go up Aaron's lonning, past where they built the Temperance Hall, and along Rotting Road. He got a dozen gangers from Lancashire, and they laid that line across the Mains like dog eating pot—just shovelling the whin bushes aside and stamping the sleepers on the bare turf and tying the rails together with bits of twine. Then one morning they got as far as the farm and there was Aaron with a rabbit-gun in his hand and a monstrous great tup in the yard behind him. Now those gangers were the sort that didn't fear neither God nor man, but they hadn't had no experience of tups, so they sent off to tell George Threlkeld. He came along and spoke to Aaron, and Aaron got his dog to chase away the tup and he and old George went into the house together. And they stayed there a gey long time. So that the men ate their bait and drank their cold tea and sent one of the lads with half a dozen billy-cans over to *The Lord Nelson* in Old Odborough to fetch them a gill of beer each, and still those two hadn't come out. And what one said to the other nobody knows, but when they did come out there was Aaron more affable than anybody ever seen him before or since, and he kicked away the tup and opened the gate, and " Good day to you, George," he says, and " Good day," says George, and he walked over to the men without a word of explanation and told them to rip up the last hundred yards of the line and carry it alongside the shore to the creek where they'd made a bit of a harbour for the ore-boats. Then Aaron closed the gate after him and leaned on it, condescending as Chloe, and said if ever he was passing that way to call in as he'd always be glad to see him. He, George, said nowt. So that's how Aaron's Lonning remains Aaron's Lonning to this day, and that's how the pit railway goes all the way round by the marsh-side, and that's how Mr Hope comes to be sitting here in my shop, coughing and wheezing like an old cart-horse. If you follow the line of my argument.'

There was silence for a couple of minutes. Then P.C. Goose-foot got up and went to the door.

'Duty calls,' he said.

A breeze was blowing down Waterloo Street bending the smoke over the road so that it caught the light from the lamps, and shook and gleamed like branches of white poplars.

'He can tell a good one, can Chunker,' said Watson Hope.

The wind, with the smell of smoke still clinging to it, passed beyond the town to muzzle among all the blackberries, the hips, the haws, and the withering willows of the damp autumnal darkness.

October

IN OCTOBER, winter begins its seige of the town. The horizons
are smudged out. Black Fell is no longer a ladder to the
loft, but a stone rolled against the gateway, blocking the road.
Boys forage among the turnip-smelling mists, scattering congregations of sparrows from the manure and straw and tree-fern-like
forests of kale. In the allotments of Rotting Road, asters, dahlias,
and Michaelmas daisies are smouldering like the rakings of a coke
fire, and the leaves of the white poplars, slipped loose from their
branches, go planing and skidding along the pavement.

This is the time when the town closes in upon itself. The rest
of England becomes foreign again. Strangers who have been
made welcome throughout the summer are now re-registered as
aliens. The old underground associations make their claims again
in club and chapel and institute. Patterns of relationships
established years ago assert their magnetic pull. This is the time
when the town subdivides against itself, makes teams and takes
sides. An internicine struggle breaks out—class against class,

party against party, denomination against denomination. The grey fields beside the slag-banks are flocked with the winter migrants of hockey, soccer, Rugby Union, and Rugby League—the word 'rugger' is never heard in Odborough. The Billiard League begins its winter run in the clubs, with dominoes and whist scampering at the side like terriers beside hounds. The Darts Knock-out opens in the pubs. In Sunday Schools and canteens there are badminton and table tennis, and the bridge cliques shuffle among the drawing-rooms of Mount Pleasant, while at St Kentigern's Young People's Fellowship, the Old Church Mid-Week Social, the Wesley Guild, the Trafalgar Road Christian Endeavour, the Baptist Brotherhood, and the Oatrigg Ex-U.M. Women's Bright Hour there are Brains Trusts, Twenty Questions, Safety-First Quizzes, and Beetle Drives.

But for me, the best of all the winter sports is the Music Festival. The Festival has been part of my life ever since it was first founded in the early twenties. My father was on the committee from the beginning : not because he had the least ear for music, but because he was always ready to support any Odborough enterprise so long as it had nothing to do with politics. (My father believed that a man should keep his political opinions to himself, not realising that that belief revealed well enough what his opinions were.) My mother, for her part, was one of the official accompanists. In 1923 she presented the Third Prize for the Boy's Solo to my own cousin, and it surprised me to see her shake hands with him on the platform as if he were a stranger. The next year I myself took part, singing in the Old Odborough Boys' School Choir, and the year after that, when I was eleven, I entered on my own in the Elocution Class. I had received no tuition, but I learnt my piece and I knew what it meant and how I meant to say it. It was a ballad of Stevenson's called, *Christmas at Sea* :

> The sheets were frozen hard and they cut the naked hand,
> The decks were like a slide where the seamen scarce could stand,
> The wind was a nor'wester, blowing squally off the sea,
> And ships and spouting breakers were the only things a-lee.

It went on to tell of a ship in a storm, close to the rocks : so close indeed, that the sailors could see the houses on shore, with the

windows lit and the chimneys smoking.   The wind whined and
piped in my own treble; the icy spray slashed across my face as I
imitated the voices of the captain and mate.   And when the poem
was ended, not a man of the crew felt a greater relief than I did.
One of them, indeed, did not feel relief at all, for the village on the
shore was his old home, and the house above the coastguard's was
the house where he was born:

> And they heaved a mighty breath, every soul on board but me,
> As they saw her nose again pointing handsome out to sea;
> But all that I could think of in the darkness and the cold,
> Was just that I was leaving home, and my folks were growing old.

I won the First Prize that year, and the next two years also—
reciting *Sherwood*, by Alfred Noyes, and *Off the Ground*, by
Walter de la Mare.   Then, after missing a year, I entered again
at the age of nearly fifteen when the test piece was a tiny four-
stanza poem by de la Mare called *Nod*.   No chance this time of
the virtuous display of memory which so impressed my uncle.   No
chance, either, to show my powers of mimicry or of dramatic
scene-painting.   *Nod* was a quiet, sleepy little poem, and so slow
that I was sure that I could have recited it in my sleep.   Indeed,
I was more than half asleep as I waited my turn at the side of the
stage.   Not from tiredness, but from nervousness, from the heat,
and from the fume of hot breath and excitement which rose from
the body of the hall.   Moreover, I was no longer a young boy
able to give his whole heart and mind to a rhyme in a story.   I
was old enough to be self-confident and self-conscious.   I was
aware of people in the audience—teachers, and my own school-
fellows.   I was aware of the other competitors in the same class.
Some of these—the only ones, indeed, with any chance against
me—were girls.   They were reciting a different test-piece—
something about fairy jam-making, sweet and sticky—but they
competed against me for the same prize.   They came from away,
and I was diverted by their elocution-school accents, and especially
by their pronunciation of the word ' sugar '.   I was diverted, too,
by their silk dresses, and by the way they fidgeted with the hem of
their skirts as they recited—this was the time when hems were at
their very highest.   I walked out when the bell rang, with the

assurance of one very much used to the job, for by this time I had recited at many concerts in every hall and Sunday School in the town. My mind was dancing a diddering polka along the gas-lights and the audience and the girls. But that did not matter : I could recite this poem by clock-work. The clock worked for two stanzas, and then stopped. I remember that I was not in the least disconcerted. My mind had come out of its dance and returned to me, and I stopped not so much because I had forgotten but because I had remembered. I was now completely aware of myself—standing on the platform, in a tense hush, and in the middle of some poem which I could not recollect. There were a score or more people in that hall who were eager to prompt me, had they dared to do so. The adjudicator, a woman, glanced at her book and read out a line. It was the first line of the stanza I had just repeated. I shook my fingers in irritated dismissal. More embarrassed, I think, than I was, she at last stumbled on the right place. I finished the poem and was awarded the Second Prize. I am satisfied that I had deserved no better. But the Odborough people were not satisfied. Why should boys have to compete against girls, they asked, not even saying the same pieces. And from that day to this the Elocution Class has been divided into two : one for boys and one for girls.

That kind of participation in the Festival ended for me at the end of schooldays, but later I helped to inscribe the prize-winners' certificates—a fact doubted by those who know my handwriting —and acted as steward in mornings and afternoons when the committee members could not attend.

I remember well those opening afternoons, often with no more than two dozen people present, and the room still cold before the steam filled the pipes. The Festival is held on the second floor up a twisting staircase of stone steps, in a hall as bare as a prison, with the windows set so high that not even an ostrich could see more than the chimney-pots through them. The old yellowing notices that have been used for thirty years are pinned to the window-sills : SILENCE and NO SMOKING and COMPETITORS ONLY. On the platform : a grand piano (hired from Furness), a couple of music stands, and the blackboard on which the numbers of class and

competitors are pinned up.   At the back of the hall in a tem-
porary look-out tower draped with red-white-and-blue muslin,
sits the adjudicator, by his side one of those slap-button brass bells
used to summon the waitress in Edwardian tea-shops.   He slaps
the bell and the first competitor, who has been sitting on her hands
for the last five minutes trying to warm them, trots to the piano
and flops into the test piece.   That first competitor is usually a girl
and is always young.   No one in Odborough, over the age of
eighteen, would enter for a piano or violin class, though the singers
will continue to compete until they are so old and so deaf that it is
only by watching the player's hands that they can keep in time
with the accompaniment.

The afternoon works its way, unenthusiastically, through the
first items : piano solo, piano duet; the Class B vocal solo, open to
those who have not yet won a prize at any Festival and don't
sound as if they ever will; the melancholy Women's Trio class, in
which the two entries have taken more trouble to match their
dresses than their voices.   The adjudicator hurries on with the
programme, addressing his remarks directly to the competitors
and taking no notice of the few stubborn season-ticket holders in
the front row.   The late October dusk condenses on the window-
panes.   Outside, the street-lamps are on, and the willows beside
the hoardings wave their yellow stripes.   The confectioners' shops
are busy serving tea to visitors—the half-lit windows steamed, the
bread sold out, the chocolate biscuits split on the window-bottom.
A sicky, sulphury mist drifts about the street, idle as the drifting
schoolgirls, whose breaths are seeming frosty in the glow of shops
and lamps.   Small children, half-tangled in their own stockings,
begin to sludge over the Bridge to first-house pictures.   A bus
up-ends its load of workmen into the Market Square, while
another waits to take a billiard team to Furness.   No one, it
would seem, thinks of the Festival at all.

On Saturday night, however, it will be different.   That is when
the choirs come out and the soloists compete for the Gold Medal.
The hall is packed, and the audience, excited, back the local
favourites as if they were horses.   They applaud the adjudicator
and listen to his comments, but it is the marks for which they are

waiting. Sometimes a competitor will be unsatisfied with the result, and once a tenor came round to the committee room threatening to knock the adjudicator's head off : Christopher Crackenthwaite threw him down the stairs. Others attend carefully to the advice given, and some, at least, profit by it. Just before the War the Gold Medal at the Odborough Festival was won for some years in succession by a young contralto from further up the county. She was later to be known as Kathleen Ferrier.

Saturday night is, above all else, the night for the Male Voice Choirs. They come in buses and sometimes by special trains— business men's choirs from Furness, club choirs from the Iron towns, and choirs of miners from the colliery coast. The Odborough Working Men's, conducted by Christopher Crackenthwaite, gathers, not at the hall, but at the club, for a final run-through. More than once, when a choir from away has failed to turn up, a message to the club has brought the men in such a hobble and scurry down the street to the hall, that not even Christopher's skilful dilly-dallying with the piano and the music stands could give them time to get their breath back. Bobbie Beck, the little barber with the sweetest bass voice in the Lake Counties, loosening his throat with a bottle of beer at the back entrance to the hall, is picked up by one of the choir and carried like a baby up the steep steps.

The men crowd the ante-rooms behind the stage, wrestling, larking, teasing, hardly giving an ear to what the other choirs are doing. But when their turn comes to sing, each man becomes prodigiously serious. The Furness conductor—the only one to use a baton—marshals his men as if they were soldiers on parade, pacing the distance between basses and tenors, grading voices by strength as chorus girls are graded by height. The miners' conductor, a great gorilla of a man, bullies and bashes the music out of his singers by brute force. Christopher Crackenthwaite, holding himself very still, seems to mesmerise his men, spreading his fingers like Svengali. They lean forward in an hypnotic hush, necks stretching, eyes periscoping up—the dwarfish club-foot alto in the front row; the six-foot baritone, who always takes his teeth out to sing, hidden away at the back. Jack Edwards, who can be relied to keep a grip on the pitch when all the rest are slithering away, makes up the left flank.   There are not more than two or three of these men who can read a note of music, and not one who would ever look at a line of poetry.   Yet, when they sing, both music and poetry are achieved.   From the tense, distorted mouths comes a single controlled line of melody; from the goggle-eyes comes a dream, a nostalgia, a fantasy, simmering up as from an underground lake of symbol.   After a pause, they scrum down and worry the heart of *Tiger, Tiger*.   The suppressed savagery of each subterranean soul gushes to the surface like struck oil.   For a little while Christopher Crackenthwaite lets the geyser spout, then, with the flick of a finger, cocks it into silence.   The hypnosis is over.   The baritone, turning round on the audience, slips his teeth in; and the alto hobbles off, slapping backs, or, when he can't reach them, bottoms; Bobbie Beck, skimming off the stage like a whippet, has his bottle out of his pocket before he is halfway through the door.

Now is the time for the adjudication.   The men surge on the stage again, eager and noisy as a football crowd.   At each commendation they laugh or applaud and turn to one another.   A good word for the altos and half a dozen lean over to shake Clubfoot by the hand.   Christopher Crackenthwaite alone remains calm, magnanimously conceding an occasional criticism by an inclination of his head.   The adjudicator passes on to the other choirs.   With each word of praise the Odborough faces darken; with each adverse comment they brighten again.   The adjudicator conceals his final decision, raising hopes and lowering them, till his listeners are as flurried as gulls swooping for biscuits.   Now all the jokes which he has used at festival after festival are brought out again.

' A pianissimo is like charity in the Bible . . . '

(' Wait for it.   Wait for it.   Shut up, Bobbie, you silly sod, he's got his eye on you.)

' . . . covereth a multitude of sins.'

The choirs bawl with laughter, and none bawls louder than Odborough, whose pianissimos, as the men well know, are as cultivated and cared for as early rhubarb.   The adjudicator consults his figures, and at once there is a groping for programmes and pencils. The silence ticks like a time-bomb.

We need not wait to hear the result, however. For if Odborough win, the Shield will be displayed in the photographer's studio in Rotting Road; if they do not, the choir will cancel its celebration Hot-pot Supper and begin to practice double-time for Blackpool. It is no good complaining that the festivals belong to the world of football pools rather than that of music, for without them there would be no choirs at all. It is the sport that binds the men together, and enables them—for a few moments at least—to hear the submerged music in their own souls. That Children's Days at the festivals encourage the display of parlour-tricks is, admittedly, true. Yet for many children in towns like Odborough the festivals are the only chance they ever get to hear the piano played properly or the voice used as it should be used. Wireless and the gramophone are no substitute. In any case, why should we ban all competition from children's music? Do not larks compete in singing?

November

EVERY YEAR, on the Fifth of November, I have the fear that it is not going to be dark enough. The watery light seems to swash up and down the sky long after the sunless sunset, as if the mists had soaked it up during the day and were now letting it ooze out again. At five o'clock the sky is brighter than it had been at three. Then the smoke begins to fall, which all day has been floating forty or fifty feet above the chimney-pots. The mirk dissolves in the mist, and the air thickens to beef-tea. A first firework explodes, hardly visible as yet. The street-lamps come on, and I wait at my window, like the hangman in *Barnaby Rudge*, watching for the first glow in the sky.

I already know where most of the bonfires will be. For weeks boys have been carrying material along the streets—branches torn out of the thorn hedges, boughs snapped off the trees in St Kentigern's Churchyard, driftwood from Oatrigg shore, old rubber tyres from the dumps, cardboard boxes and straw packing begged from the grocer's.

Tommy Dale, on *Crown* Green, spring-cleans his warehouse every November, tossing the rubbish out of the upstairs sliding doorway into the street below—packing-cases, cartons, showcards, corrugated cardboard, egg wrappings, old sacks, rope, dates gone bad, and cornflakes that the rats have got at. Mr Snoot, at Mount Pleasant, before he died counting *The Crown* Green stars, used to give his privet hedge its last trimming of the season just at this time, knowing that he would not have to trouble about sweeping up the clippings. All these finds are dragged on the end of ropes or carted on little bogeys to be stacked on waste lots or hidden in back-yards. Near the time, some of the groups will set up all-day watches on their pile, for these lads steal from one another like building rooks. There are stories, too, of bonfires kindled the day before, and of the Coronation Bonfire on Black Fell, which should have been lit by the squire of the next village, and was fired before his eyes by a troup of Odborough lads after he had toiled up two thousand rheumaticky feet to fulfil his duty.

I usually start my walk at about six-thirty, by which time the smaller bonfires are already lit. Timothy Tyson is letting off his fireworks in his grandfather's back-yard, safely bolted against other spectators. In every one of the otherwise pitch-dark back-streets there are two or three private burnings, no bigger than a night-watchman's brazier, each with its half dozen children clustered around. These terraces of the nineties are the newest part of the New Town: the front streets wide, with doors and windows railed and priveted from the pavement, but the backs narrow and conspiratorial. Children, here, are not allowed to run with the rougher tribes from beyond *The Crown* Green, but gather, cautiously, in little back-door congregations of known and approved names. The cabbalistic flames flicker up from their hands.

Slate walls glow red and burning shavings sail above the roofs of coal-house and closet. A *Silver Fountain* distempers the roughcast with eau-de-nil in which corners of window and window-sill are hacked clean and black. The sticks of a back-yard lilac jut black against a magnesium glow, like a sweep's brush thrust out of a wash-house chimney. Boys, anonymous as nigger minstrels, smudge across from shadow to glow—in balaclava helmets and old jerseys and head-shawls, seeming a subterranean nocturnal subspecies of man emerging from ash-pits and tool-sheds, rag-and-bone warehouses and stonemason's yards.

I go first down Railway Road to the Dunner Banking, where once there used to be the town's biggest fire, but which lately has lost its popularity—perhaps because so often an unexpectedly high tide has swept the pile away on the day before the Fifth. Tonight, there are only half a dozen lads prodding with iron bars at cardboard boxes. A few scattered clinkers throw a faint glow on the sour turf, and the lamps of the Ironworks Railway traipse along the edge of the marsh, spilling dribbles of light into the pools and channels. Out in the estuary, a reddening of the mist shows where a bonfire is burning on the Lancashire shore.

I leave the Banking and set off towards the slag-bank end of Odborough, where families have gone on living for three or four generations, and where street is banded against street in vendettas old as the town. The castle-keep of the gas-holder glooms up in the light of the huge denominational bonfire by the Catholic School. What event in history—I wonder—do they think they are celebrating? Women's faces, beaked and predatory, crane out of crannies and eyries. Boys defend their bonfires with the territorial instinct of a nesting bird, brandishing broom-handles with ends glowing from the fire, and repulsing strangers with a cannonade of crackerjacks. A crowd of mothers and small sisters barricades the street, leaving an open space like a parade ground in front of the fire. Big sisters, their throats swathed in scarves of smoke, scream and Highland Fling among the outskirts of the embers, seeming to draw whizzbangs and fizzers towards them as if their ankles were magnets. A young man from the club-house of the Knights of St Columba keeps the kettle boiling with another sackload, as the bonfire, with a tripod of wooden fencing and old railway sleepers at its heart, roars and belches, and the darkness coughs with sulphur and smuts. A rocket, fired from a tipped-over milk-bottle, jets across the street at garter-height, and fizzes out against a parlour door in a skitter of skirts and swearing. An atomic banger explodes behind me. It is time, I judge, to move on.

.   .   .

The Crown Green is strident with light, but not from a bonfire. The great fire to which, years ago, Mr Snoot used to contribute all the broken bamboo tables and horse-hair-bottomed chairs of Happy Homes Ltd., is now replaced by the hobby-horses. Only a few boys claim their right of way for a miserable smoking of paper and cardboard on the edge of the grass, watched resentfully and apprehensively by the fair-ground proprietors. For many years, now, the hobby-horses have been coming to the Green about the middle of October and staying until nearly Christmas, when they move along to Furness. But if the Miss Snoots ever came to this part of the town—as, indeed, they never do, for they despise it more than they despise one another—they would find the fair very different from the one they used to know. There are no longer the blue-and-yellow horses, seemingly suspended from spiral-fluted brass rods, the ostriches with leather saddles, the cocks and hens with seats between their wings to carry a child—only racing cars that surge and dip over stomach-turning waves. There is no longer the steam organ, with little waxwork minstrels banging gongs and triangles in time with the music— only a loudspeaker booming and howling. There are no longer coconut shies and rifle ranges and hoopla stalls—only a row of pin-tables and gambling machines where grey, obsessed women shove in handful upon handful of pennies. When the hobbyhorses are on the Green there is always a shortage of copper in the town shops. The cars switchback round, almost empty, for tonight the children are too busy, and the soldiers and factory girls are not yet on the prowl. The gramophone bawls out more mechanical than ever, now that it is dissociated from human bustle and laughter. The sound clangs and scrapes against the front doors of Victoria Street and rattles the bedroom windows, hammering against ears long since immune to the noise of buzzer and foundry but having no protection at all against this.

Tommy Dale, however, has protection, sitting in his back-shop

parlour, deaf as buttered toast. Years before, when his shop was
open until half-past nine on Saturday nights, he would leave the
door ajar—cold as it might be—to listen to the hobby-horse organ.
For it was not just the pub-songs that the organ rendered, but
The War March of the Priests and the overture to *Zampa* and
The Hallelujah Chorus, so that even the elders of the Methodist
Chapels would pause and lean on their walking-sticks as the
gongers and cymbalists whacked and tinkled. Then Isaac
Crossthwaite would drive up with his potato machine, and the
women would come from the houses to buy platefuls for supper,
and Marmaduke Crackenthwaite, Christopher's father, would
treat the girls on the roundabouts, three or four at a time, and slip
hot potatoes into their pockets and muffs, and keep on squeezing
and prodding them as he sang:

Who is the King of Glory?

That was the time when the whole town came out every Saturday night. All the men who never set foot in a public-house, nor
in one another's private houses, either, would take their walking-
sticks on one arm and their wives on the other, and parade the full
diagram of Waterloo Street, Trafalgar Road, the Market Square,
and *The Crown* Green. They stopped before the shop-windows,
and raised bowler hats, and discussed Home Missions and the
British Empire, and listened to the Salvation Army band. The
streets, then, were respectable, popular and proud of themselves—
the promenade and assembly of a people who still regarded with
moral suspicion any indoor entertainment not connected with the
chapel. And on Bank Holidays, mornings and evenings, the
streets were thronged with families. Friends from opposite ends
of the town, who did not meet at any other time of the year,
greeted and questioned one another. Grandmothers, emerging
only once or twice a summer, observed the changes. To Mr Dale
the empty streets of the modern Bank Holiday are a sign of lost
gaiety and pride.

.   .   .

I move away from the Green into the streets below the slag-
bank, worming back into the past of the town, nuzzling into old

alleys and entries as a child nuzzles into its mother. Here, at night, the world loses its present-day look. The bonfires throw a flapping glare over scenes which have scarcely changed since bonfires were first lit in these streets—Victorian shop-fronts, with spiral frames; heavy sandstone lintels over parlour doors that open straight on to the pavement; old lamp-standards up which seventy-five years ago, my father used to swamble. These, indeed, are the streets of *his* childhood, not of mine, and the children here are older than I will ever be. But I pass, now, through the entry-tunnel beside the Bible Christian Chapel into Furnace Road where my cousins lived, beside the road laid down by our grandfather, and where, every year, they gave a great show of fireworks to friends and neighbours. Fireworks were not so common in the 1920s in Odborough. Few parents could afford more than a half-crown box; most could afford none. My cousins, however, had a grandfather (not mine) in Durham who sold fireworks at his ironmonger's shop, so that every November they used to hire part of the field which lay opposite the house, in among the allotments and hen-runs behind Back Trafalgar Road. All the choir-boys of St Kentigern's were there, probing the bonfire, while the Slag-bank Rovers scrimmaged in the road and climbed the fence to get a better view. Upstairs, at the bedroom window, my cousin's great-aunt kept watch over the road, rapping the window-sill with a walking-stick whenever a stranger tried to gate-crash into the field.

For my own part, I cared little for fireworks. I disliked the fizz and the bang; I disliked the forty-flappers that hopped about like frogs, and the whizzers that suddenly snapped at your heels. *Catherine Wheels* I liked well enough, safely pinned against a wood-shed, or a rocket, sent skedaddling up to blow off its harm on the sky—though for nearly a minute after, I would go about with my head bowed and my hands clasped behind my neck in case the rocket-stick fell on me. My aunt, seeing this, would come over and give me a box of coloured matches which glowed a railway-signal red or green, or a packet of sparklers which I could whirl round my head like a red-hot poker, weaving little comet's tails in the darkness. My uncle, who believed that all boys

M

loved bangs, would have laughed at this, but, luckily, he took no notice of me, being too busy clearing a space for cannons or setting *Roman Candles* in the neck of medicine bottles.   So that I was left to nibble at the edge of the bonfire smoking my lungs like a kipper, kicking cinders back into the fire, or stoking it with broken-off twigs and leaves of privet.   Then I would slip away from the crowd and trail off to the far fence, and watch the firelight gleaming on the tarred hen-huts and the autumnal tatters of the white poplars.   Over in the allotments one or two other small bonfires flared up, a scurry of sparks whirling from the poplars and currant bushes like a flight of disturbed starlings.   The old iron bedsteads that made up much of the fencing held a black cut-out pattern against the flames.

That is what I saw then and that is what I see now, though my cousins have left the town and my aunt this very month was buried under the winter heliotrope in St Kentigern's Churchyard. Wooden garages have taken the place of the hen-huts, and the poplars by Ironworks Villa have grown into a jungle, but, at night, nothing else seems changed.   Not a brick has been laid on a brick in these parts for the last thirty years.

The family bonfires are still burning on the allotments, and above Iron Green and Oatrigg and the new estate of Old Odborough I can see the glow of larger fires organised by neighbours and street committees.   But these do not interest me now. I make my way still farther back into the past, going towards the Iron Green and the old swamp which was there before the first roads were made, and the first foundations dug.   The geese, not yet shut up for the night, file across the Green, ostentatiously unperturbed by the occasion, though every now and then one of them cranes after the smuts that float past like luminous butterflies.

And now, beyond *The Iron Man* and at the foot of the slag-bank, I see a fire which looks as if it might have burned there, once a year, ever since the Vikings first landed on this coast a thousand years ago.   The slag gleams like basalt or the lava of Iceland under the Aurora Borealis, and the 'flash' at its foot reflects the light like the waters of a fiord.   Here, surely, however little it may be understood, something of the old ritual remains.

These lads no longer belong to the twentieth century—they belong with the Vikings and the Celts and the men of the Isle of Man; with the men who lit the Beltane Fires and the Midsummer Fires and the fires of the First of May.

The meaning of the old ceremonial is well known today : how the god who burned in the bonfires was a vegetation god, often a tree spirit, while the fire represented the sun and the whole vital and fructifying power of light and warmth. There was a time when they used to stuff cartwheels or tar-barrels with straw, set them alight, and roll them blazing down the side of this slag-bank. In other places, disks were cut out of wood, sometimes notched with rays like the sun, and thrown high into the air, making a burning arc in the sky. Even today we still have *Catherine Wheels*. All of which, beyond doubt, portray the wheeling round of the sun in the course of the seasons.

The rituals have a sexual significance, too, for fire has always been a sexual symbol. The Midsummer Fires were often lit by a man and a woman who had just been married, and engaged couples would jump together, hand in hand, through the smoke to ensure that their union would be fruitful. That significance continues, though the fruitfulness of union is no longer so much valued. For the night still arouses a subdued sexual excitement, half-concealed, half-acknowledged. When the young men start to throw whizzbangs about they do not now throw them at one another—they throw them at the girls. And in doing so, they are interpreting quite correctly at least one of the purposes of this ritual.

I am not suggesting that there is a mystical blood-and-fire cult hidden in the modern Fifth of November festivals, or that they represent any very valuable survival of folk-culture. Maybe they would have died out altogether except for the encouragement of the fireworks manufacturers. Yet the excitement of a boy must be much the same whether his bonfire is a sacramental rite or merely a few boxes set alight in the back-yard. The excitement, the enjoyment, is more primitive, more enduring than the ritual which inspires it or the symbol which inspired the ritual. So that these lads beside the slag-bank belong to an Odborough older than even the name of Odborough; to a town which is not yet a town; to an iron landscape which has not yet found its iron.

The screes of slag slant up into the mist and the smoke, and glaciers of shadow slide down its surface almost into the lap of the fire. The pond flares like a river of hell, with old hoops and buckets and willows writhing in the water like the damned. The fire burns low, though the boys poke it with iron bars torn out of the railings, or kick little volcanoes of clinkers into the air. The glow is being drained out of the sky as the bonfires are dying down everywhere. Rockets are rarer, and the former machine-gun spatter of the fireworks has now given way to a few isolated bangs from street to street. The stucco of *The Iron Man* sulks back into its usual smeared khaki. The back streets are dark as tunnels again. Then, suddenly, the furnaces release their one big firework. The slag fountains up in a thousand-pounds' worth of *Crimson Stars* and *Golden Rain*. Streets, chimneys, doorways, the pub, the Green, the ruins of *The White Mouse*, the old iron dump behind it, the slag-bank, the flash, the willows, junk, and rubble are all gilded, trinketed, coroneted, and glorificated in the blarney of the light.

The glow ebbs as fast as it flared, though the mist still retains a rusty smudge. The boys hack and coax their last cinders on the edge of the dark.

December

IF YOU want to annoy a man from the provinces, call him
'provincial'. For the word, used in this sense, implies the
smug, the narrow, the short-sighted; implies a mere second-
hand, second-rate, out-of-date existence, a bad copy of the life of
the capital. Yet why should life in the provinces be a bad copy?
Or, indeed, any sort of copy? There is nothing at all odd in
being provincial. Most men today, in England and elsewhere,
are provincial. Most men of all times always have been provincial. It is the metropolitan who is the oddity.

[*Tommy Dale stands at his shop door talking to Councillor
Quorum. A blizzard of cotton-wool is glued to the window-pane,
and tinsel strews hoar-frost on the crackers, glacé cherries, and
Christmas puddings.*

'*What we need in this town,*' *he says,* '*is a broader outlook.*'
—*He gazes across* The Crown *Green, now emptied of the hobby-
horses, to the Social Club, the blackened orchard, and the new gas-
holder beyond St Joseph's*—'*What we need,*' *he repeats,* '*is vision.*']

For the oddest thing about the metropolis is that it has become the reason for its own existence. It is there merely because it is there. Other towns exist through some obvious geographical cause : Odborough because of its iron ore; Wigan because of its coal; Burton-on-Trent because the Triassic Period left deposits of gypsum which made the water ideal for brewing. The metropolis, to begin with, grew up because of some similar topographical advantage : because it was on a ford or an estuary and was a convenient centre for trade. But it has gone on growing of its own accord. It puts on suburb after suburb like layers of superfluous fat. So that its inhabitants scarcely know why they are there; they have lost the sense of a vital and purposeful link with the land on which they live. If their city were scooped off the surface of the earth in a huge ladle-spoon and slapped down a hundred miles away, they would scarcely notice any difference.

The metropolis, too, is so large that it ceases to be a unit, and its people cease to be a community. It splits up into zones. With each separate zone we may have uniformity of habit, income, and outlook. But some of the zones scarcely communicate one with the other. They speak differently, think differently, dress differently. Even the uniformity within the zone is often merely of the surface. The people do not really know one another. They have gathered from various parts of the country and pitched their caravans side by side, but they no more belong to one place than do the gipsies. They share, sometimes, much the same opinions and prejudices, catching fashions like the 'flu and wearing today's morals cut like today's skirts. But it is a unity of the head rather than of the whole body. Their branches are together; their roots are apart.

['*I tell you it's coming right enough,*' says Chunker Wilson to Bob Hope. '*See here!*'

He takes a handful of shells out of his pocket and throws them on the billiard table.

'*Cockles!*'

'*Unfit for human consumption,*' says P.C. Goosefoot, who was standing by the door into the street.

'*Who's claiming to be human?*'

' You'll not have to be selling them, any road.'

' I will not.   But if you'd like a taste for your tea tomorrow, just call in with a half-pint mug.'

' I'd rather have mussels myself,' says the constable.   ' Half a dozen mussels roast on a shovel are a comfort and a blessing on a cold night.'

' Or slipped on the hot iron in the foundry while the castings are cooling,' says Bob Hope.

' Listen,' says Chunker.   ' Them cockles came in the early 1920s—just at the worst of the slump.   There was one winter when three men in four were out of work in Odborough and the kids were going to school with no more than dry bread and tea without milk.   That's when they found the cockles.   There'd always been a few, of course, up and down the Dunner and off the Point, but that year they found a bed as rank as wicks.   They just had to wade out to the bank, dig up the shells and wash them in sea-water, and they could fill a sack in five minutes.   Dunner cockles and Oatrigg flooks saved Odborough from starvation that winter.   Like manna in the wilderness.'

' Then the cockles died off,' says Bob.   ' What with over-digging and sea-pies.'

' And pollution,' adds the policeman.

" Mebbe,' says Chunker.   ' But now they're on the way back. That's why I say the slump's coming.   Mark my words.']

The people of Odborough know nothing of unity of opinion. They are divided perpetually, one against another in politics and religion, in social and family quarrels. They band together, change sides, swap partners, bicker, and contradict. Two men who from Monday to Saturday support and applaud one another at the Conservative Club will sulk on Sundays into doctrinal separation. Two more, who once a week are brethren in Christ, will hate each other the rest of the time as secretaries of the two antagonistic brass bands. There is dissension, argument, back-biting, and spite. If there is less division of class here than else-where, it is only because the society of Odborough is not wide enough in range to allow much of such division. So far as money goes, there is little difference, now, between those who consider themselves petty bourgeois and those who consider themselves working-class. The maiden ladies of Balmoral Road, who keep themselves TO themselves, are far worse off than the miners and the furnace men. And the few who sit on a higher step—bank managers, doctors, and the bosses at the works—are almost all off-comes and not Odborough people at all.

Yet the unity of the town no more depends on equal income than it depends on agreed opinion. It is the unity of the breed, of the clan, of fledglings hatched in the same nest. For all these people have behind them the same memories of childhood, the same shared backgrounds. They have been fed and watered by the same weather. They have all felt the same excitement queue-ing for the same children's matinée outside *The Wreck*; they have all run over the Railway Bridge, hearts back-firing like motor-bikes, fearing that they would miss the same train. They have known the tension that comes at a time of local anxiety : the day the tide broke through the sea-wall; the day the viaduct was found unsafe; the week when roads and railway were blocked by snow and not a soul could enter the town for six days. Certain sights and sounds are familiar to all of them. They have all lain awake at night, at some year of their lives, aware of the smells of the marsh and the foundry drifting in the mist like the conscious-ness of Original Sin. They know how the slag-bank blocks one end of the streets and how Black Fell bulges up over the other end. Every step out of doors takes them through a landscape charged with the associations of childhood.

[*Mrs Grice, venturing up to the* Jubilee Jug *for her Christmas bottle of rum, watches the geese, that have so few hours left of life, strutting through what was once the marsh meadow of willows and milk-maids.*] All that they see—shop, school, chapel, ware-house yard—takes its memory from the lives of the people round them. [*Contralto Ethel, on her way to carol practice, walks along the empty Cumberland Road in a flare of naphtha, and is chased by Christopher Crackenthwaite's dead father into the back-street behind the chapel.*]

When a generation has been reared in a closed environment like Odborough, it matters little that one man, when he grows up, should turn left and another turn right, that one should choose Bach and another billiards. For, in spite of contradictions of taste and temperament, they are all stirred by the same images. The Town Clock strikes with the significance it always had, and death, for each of them, has the smell of the winter heliotrope.

[*The western sky is soaked in cochineal. John Dodder, in Rotting Road, sees the Pleasure Ground poplars scratched black on red like a drawing on a Christmas card. Johnnie Moss, from the Market Square, looking up at the east window of St Kentigern's, watches the sunset blazing in the nave.*]

Odborough is out of date, of course, one of the last, half-dead-in-the-bud shoots of a huge decaying trunk. It belongs to a world soon to be as distant as that of Merrie England. Its landscape is as archaic as the columns of Rome. The Iron Age is taking its place beside the Stone Age.

[*Bogey Burrows, patrolling the slag-bank in the brown of the morning, peers through a pair of old army binoculars at where, miles out on the marshes, the wild geese are grazing like a flock of sheep.*]

Yet the world will still need industry, and—if England is not to become one lubberly suburb, like a great, fat, neutered cat—it will still need its industrial towns. There is no reason why they should be excessively large, for everything we want in even the most comfortable of civilisations could be produced by small or medium-sized communities. The power-source of the future will not be the coalfield, but the atomic village. The new towns may well be as clean and fresh as a dale hamlet. Slag, smoke, dust, slums, stagnant drains, dumps, slumps, waste, poverty, and tuberculosis will no longer—one hopes—be necessary. Yet the gain will be less than the loss if the new towns cannot hold on to that organic unity, that wholeness, which we still find in the old towns.

[' *Now then, Chris,' says Bob Hope. ' What about a ticket in the Christmas Draw?'*

' *What's it for?* ' *asks Christopher Crackenthwaite. ' Spying glasses for the three sweet Snoots?* '

' *Christmas Box for John Dodder.*']

Christopher pulls out his half-crown.]

For the sense of community, of interdependence of life with life, family with family, trade with trade, did not come to an end at the Industrial Revolution. You will still find it in every town where livelihood depends on the one industry and that industry depends on place—on the rock, on the soil, on the sea, on the climate : coal- and iron-mining towns, steel towns, ports and fisheries, textile towns; towns built, it would seem, not of bricks and mortar, but of pig-iron, wool, jute, leather, or clay. These retain something of the character of an England that has died out not only in the cities but also in the country. [*In the three-yard-square front gardens of Balmoral Road the winter jasmine is already in flower.*] The villages, only too often, no longer belong to the country. They have been bought up by the towns. They are populated by the commuters and retired pork-butchers. The young drift away; the lanes are full of strangers. But in the little industrial towns the family pattern is stronger, the breed unmixed. No well-to-do tradesmen come to them for retirement. The old live there because there is nowhere else for them to be old in. There are no picture postcards, no day trippers, no girls with dogs being photographed beside cars. The town is compact, self-contained, self-reliant, almost, as a mediaeval village. For everyone lives on industry, as once they lived on the land, and the slump is feared as once a bad harvest was feared. No serf was ever bound more firmly to the land than is an iron-ore miner, a collier, or an Urban District Council town clerk.

[*The cortege, like a black cable, twists from Rotting Road along Trafalgar Street to the Bible Christian Chapel. Old Mr Sprout, directing his grandson's thoughts up yonder, has gone there himself.*]

Yet even in Odborough the pattern is partly broken. There is, as it were, a hole in the bag, and the hole, paradoxically, is at the top. For if a child is successful at school he will very likely leave the town. The Grammar School creams off the best brains of each adolescent generation, sends them to colleges and universities, and rarely calls them back. The educated men and women of the town are almost entirely off-comers—parsons, doctors, teachers, civil service and local government officials, managers, inspectors, technical advisers, and all the rest. They sometimes come from very similar towns and have an understanding of the people. They sometimes take an *ex-officio* part in local life and become grafted on the main stem. A bank manager, for instance, almost as soon as he arrives, is expected to be treasurer of half a dozen different societies. Yet this means that nearly all those activities which keep the town mentally awake have to be in the hands of those who were not born there. For the home-born young men and girls who might have given the town its growing edge of awareness are themselves strangers in a hundred other places. So that there is growing up in the provinces a generation of dispossessed intellectuals—not rootless, but uprooted—who sometimes find it hard to come to sympathy with the people among whom they live because they have not shared with them the background of childhood. The intellectual cleavage in our society—which is far more dangerous than the economic cleavage—is exaggerated in small towns because so many of the top stratum are strangers. Were this not the case, the small town is perhaps the best place of all for bringing together men of different mental abilities. There is so much shared experience between them, so much which matters equally, if not in the same way, to all.

[*Derek Dale walks up the frosty drive of St Kentigern's and enters the church. It is the time of Morning Prayer and he feels that people are looking at him enquiringly. He takes a back pew, kneels down, and repeats The Lord's Prayer. What would they all say, he wonders, if they knew that he has tabulated his objections to Christianity like a Bill of Rights. He sits back and begins to recite them in order, and suddenly, in a surge of astonishment and relief, finds that they no longer mean anything at all.*]

The small provincial towns, we are told, are anachronisms—dull, old-fashioned, stick-in-the-mud, blinkered and blindfolded in ignorance of a world they do not know they are part of. Yet it is in just what metropolitan man calls dullness that their value lies. They are stick-in-the-mud because they still believe there is mud to stick in. They are slow to change because so much about them seems to change very little. They are comparatively immune from freaks and panics of fashion. They gaze on a landscape which—so far as it can be said of anything in this world—has a look of permanence.

[*The elder Miss Snoot, who is to leave Mount Pleasant—having had to sell it, under pressure of poverty, to the new headmaster of Rotting Road Boys'—looks for the last time over the roofs at those hills which tomorrow she will look at over the railway.*]

For there is a fear in the metropolis like a malignant growth. Drop half a dozen hydrogen bombs on London and where would it be? Would there be anything left that even next summer's swallows could recognise? But if a bomb were dropped on Odborough—and surely no one will waste £1,000,000 on so insignificant a destruction—the landscape would show little change. The town might be gone, but Black Fell would still be there, and the sea and the marshes and the rocks. And except for a few roofs, chimneys, fields, and trees, the view from my bedroom window is almost the same as it was at the end of the Ice Age.

[*Tank Tyson walks home from the Foundry across the Goose Green in a hoary, purple twilight, lobbing leg-breaks along the cracked pitches of the slag. 'Next month,' he says to himself, 'the month after next will be the last month without cricket.' Though, as he had decided last September, all months, from now on, will be without cricket for him. He breaks back from an old sardine tin between the bat and the yard-door of* The Furnace Arms. *'Or, mebbe,' he says, 'One more season, like. Considering.'*]

The provincial towns have a way of being oblivious to a crisis until the crisis is over; they are reluctant to face facts because they know that what are facts today are often fairy-tales tomorrow. Within the narrow circle of the small town the small townsman is concerned with what has always been the concern of the majority of men—life, work, and family, within the pattern of one place, one set of physical circumstances, one group of people. It is not the narrowness of outlook which is the danger to provincial life but a superficial broadening. Television, cinema, radio, newspapers, all the treacherous persuasion of advertisement, depict an enormous, standardised, non-local landscape of repetitive sub-hives.   It is the dilution of local tradition and local culture by the tasteless, odourless, colourless, bottled slop of the metropolis which is starving the provinces.   They are being continually confronted with pictures of a way of life which, while it may be desirable for those for whom it is designed, is inappropriate and unsatisfying for them.   The village envies the town, the town envies the city, the city envies the metropolis.   The wife of the Urban District Sanitary Inspector, with a skyline of 300,000,000-year-old rocks to look at from her kitchen window, day-dreams of shops and buses and afternoon tea in the roof-garden café.

[*Daphne Dempster, pushing her pram along the pavements of the new estate, sets off on her every-other-daily trip to next-door to the slag-bank to see how her mother is getting on with the mince-pies.*]

For it is the wide view which is the illusion and the narrow one which is nearer the truth.   Within the circle of the small town, indeed, we can see the basic structure of human society which is lost sight of in the metropolis.   We can see the soil out of which the food comes and the rock out of which the ore comes.   We can see how one trade depends on another.   We can see how obligations and responsibilities rivet craft to craft, family to family.

[*Canon Olds finishes the last stanza of the last book of the* Gerusalemme Liberata.

> *Così vince Goffredo; ed a lui tanto*
> *avanza ancor de la dïurna luce,*
> *ch'a la città gia liberata——*]

The pattern is still visible, moreover, as a pattern not of classes and functions but of men and women.   A man is not merely seen as a member of a class, a brick in a wall, because he is known to be a brick in so many different walls.   The Chairman of the Co-operative Society Committee may denounce John Dale, the grocer, as a bourgeois exploiter of workers, but thoroughly appreciates his donkey-dropper off-breaks when he plays for Wilson's Willows.   Here, in Odborough, each man remains closely integrated with his fellows whether he likes it or not.   He may try to disassociate himself; he may try to pretend that he does not belong.   He may become an anarchist, a heretic, or even a

poet. But they will not be impressed. They knew him long
before he put on such airs. They knew him at school; they knew
his parents; they know where he was brought up. They may
laugh at him and even despise him, but they will disown him.
He is still one of them, whatever he may feel about it, so long as
he stays among them.

[*Timothy Tyson knocks on the door at the end of the second
verse of* ' While Sheperds '.

' *Ought to be ashamed of himself,*' *says Mrs Quorum.* ' *Singing carols with his gran'pa just buried.*']

In Odborough a man may seem a long way from the centre of
things, but he is closer to the heart of things. [*The Salvation
Army Band plays* Christians Awake *outside the Working Men's*].
He sees the soil, the hills, all about him. He knows the farms
that his milk comes from. He can watch the potatoes from
furrow to Tommy Dale's shop. He can trace his roofing slates
back to the quarries, his drainpipes back to the ore, his table and
chairs back to the trees. [*The Christmas Eve bells are swaying
like boats in the pink, slag-lit mist.*] He has before him continual
reminders of the rock out of which he grows. The fields and
mines are next-door, the fells are on the horizon. He has no
illusions of the self-sufficiency of man. He knows where he comes
from; he knows what he is up against. [*The rain falls slantingly
through the steam of the Ironworks reservoir.*]

.   .   .

' La città gia liberata,' says Canon Olds; the city now made
free.